The Visual Pigments

THE VISUAL PIGMENTS

by

H. J. A. DARTNALL
B.Sc., Ph.D., F.R.I.C.

Head, Visual Research Division,
Ophthalmological Research Unit (Medical Research Council),
Institute of Ophthalmology.

LONDON: METHUEN & CO. LTD.
NEW YORK: JOHN WILEY & SONS, INC.

First published in 1957
Printed in Great Britain by the Pitman Press, Bath
Methuen Catalogue No. 4144/u

Contents

695

TO

MY MOTHER

AND

FATHER

Acknowledgments

The author wishes to record his thanks to Miss D. J. Taylor for assistance in preparing the original illustrations. He also desires to acknowledge his indebtedness to the Editorial Boards and Proprietors of the following scientific journals, and to the authors concerned, for permission to reproduce the following figures:

Journal of Physiology: Figs. 1.9, 2.6, 2.7, 2.11, 2.13, 3.9, 5.8, 5.9, 6.1, 6.2, 6.3, 6.6, 6.7, 6.8, 6.9, 6.10, 7.1, 7.2, 7.4, 7.9 and Plate 1.

Journal of General Physiology: Figs. 2.2, 2.3, 2.4, 2.5, 3.10, 3.11, 4.5, 4.6, 5.2, 5.3, 5.4, 5.6, 5.7.

Proceedings A of the Royal Society: Figs. 3.2 and 3.4.

Biochemical Journal: Figs. 2.12, 3.7, 4.3.

Optica Acta: Figs. 7.5, 7.10, 7.11.

Science: Figs. 2.9 and 2.10.

Acknowledgment is also made to Messrs. H. K. Lewis for permission to reproduce Fig. 1.1 from Eugene Wolf's *Anatomy of the Eye and Orbit*, and to the University of Chicago Press for permission to reproduce Fig. 1.2 from S. L. Polyak's *The Retina* (Copyright (1941) University of Chicago).

CHAPTER ONE

Introduction and Methods

ANATOMY OF THE EYE

THE DIOPTRIC APPARATUS

For an organism to have a sense of sight, as distinct from a mere awareness of light, it must possess a means of forming an image of the external scene on its light-sensitive cells. This problem has been solved by Nature in more than one way but, for the present purpose, it is sufficient to describe briefly the main features of a vertebrate eye.

In Fig. 1.1 is shown a horizontal section of the human eye. The eyeball, an approximate sphere of 1 in. diameter, has a tough opaque outer tunic called the sclera. In life only a portion of this is visible (the white of the eye) but it actually covers the whole surface except for a circular transparent portion, called the cornea, through which light can enter. The cornea (0·5 mm thick) is of rather greater curvature than the sclera, and has a refractive index of 1·38.

The space behind the cornea, known as the anterior chamber, is filled with a transparent aqueous humour having a refractive index similar to that of water (1·33). The cornea and aqueous humour together are equivalent in refractive power to a lens of about 43 dioptres. (A 1 dioptre lens has a focal length of 1 metre, a 2 dioptre lens, one of 0·5 metre, and so on.)

Behind the anterior chamber is a transparent, double convex body called the crystalline lens. This is composed of concentric layers of tissue, the curvature, hardness and refractive index of which increase towards the centre, the refractive index increasing from 1·38 to 1·41.

The space behind the lens is filled with the vitreous humour, a transparent jelly with the same refractive index as the aqueous. In contact with the vitreous humour is the retina, the sensitive layer upon which the visual image is formed.

Between the retina and the sclera is the choroid, a soft, brown, extremely vascular layer containing melanin pigment. The function of the choroid is mainly nutritive but it is similar to erectile tissue and plays a part in the regulation of the intraocular pressure.

By means of the ciliary muscle the form, and hence the power, of the crystalline lens can be varied so that, whatever the distance of the object regarded, a sharp image is cast on the retina. The total power

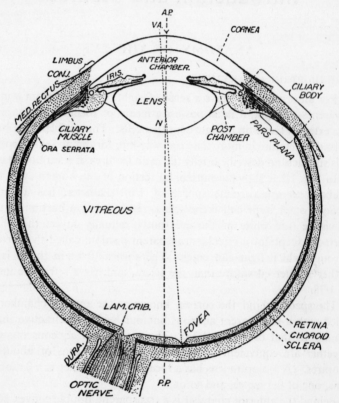

FIG. 1.1. Horizontal section of the human eye.
(*Wolff*, 1948)

of the resting eye (that is, when relaxed for distant vision) is about 60 dioptres. In a young child, whose lens is still soft and pliable, a further 14 dioptres of power can be added by the maximum effort of accommodation. Throughout life the lens hardens, however, and in elderly persons all accommodation has been lost and aids to reading are necessary.

The amount of light which enters the eye is controlled by the iris, a membrane having a circular aperture called the pupil. The iris has the form of a very shallow truncated cone, the pupillary border of which is supported by the lens. In darkness the pupil expands to its greatest diameter, about 8 mm, while in very bright light it contracts to about 1·5 mm. Since the focal length of the eye is about 20 mm, the effective aperture can thus vary between $f.2·5$ and $f.13$, giving a range of nearly 30:1 in the amount of light admitted.

THE RETINA AND ITS CONNECTIONS TO THE BRAIN

The retina covers the inside of the posterior part of the eyeball. Over most of its surface the retina is only loosely attached but it is firmly bound along its periphery at the *ora serrata* and also at the *lamina cribrosa* (through which pass the fibres of the optic nerve).

Although the retina is only one or two hundredths of an inch thick, it has a very complicated structure. A diagrammatic section is shown in Fig. 1.2. In essence, the retina has two parts, a sensory neuro-epithelium consisting of the percipient elements (the 'rods' and 'cones') and an inner, extremely complex, arrangement of nervous tissue, similar both in structure and function to the central nervous system of which it is, in fact, an outlying part.

It is in the rod-cone layer that the image cast upon the retina by the dioptric apparatus of the eye is in sharpest focus. The light thus falling on the rods and cones causes changes in them which disturb the electrical equilibrium of the outer nuclear layer (Fig. 1.2).

The electrical changes so initiated are subject to mutual interaction within the nervous layers of the retina. The ultimate messages from the retina are transmitted by the optic nerve fibres. The bundles of nerve fibres proceeding from each eye divide at the optic chiasma, so that those serving the left-hand halves of each retina continue to the left side of the brain, and those serving the right-hand halves, to the right side. Since (as in the camera) the retinal image is not only inverted but also laterally transposed, this means that the right-hand visual fields of both eyes are represented in the left brain, and vice versa. Consequently, because the left brain relates to the right-hand side of the body, the projection on the brain of the right visual field (for example) is topographically close to those areas serving the right musculature and sensory systems.

On arrival at the brain the electric changes propagated through the optic nerve fibres give rise, in some unknown and perhaps

3

unknowable way, to the sensations of vision, i.e. form, brightness, colour and saturation.

FIELDS OF STUDY

In the study of vision proper, that is of the processes which ensue as the result of the formation of an image on the retina, diverse methods have been used. In much of the work the main object has

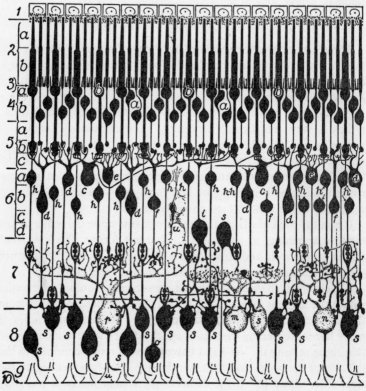

FIG. 1.2. Diagrammatic section of the primate retina.

Layers: 1, pigment epithelium; 2 (*a*), (*b*), rod and cone layer; 3, outer limiting membrane; 4 (*a*), (*b*), outer nuclear layer; 5 (*a*), (*b*), (*c*), outer plexiform layer; 6 (*a*), (*b*), (*c*), (*d*), inner nuclear layer; 7, inner plexiform layer; 8, ganglion cell layer; 9, optic nerve fibres; 10 inner limiting membrane.

Nerve cells: (*a*), rods; (*b*), cones; (*c*), horizontal cells; (*d*), (*e*), (*f*), (*h*), bipolar cells; (*i*), (*l*), amacrine cells; (*m*), (*n*), (*o*), (*p*), (*s*), ganglion cells; (*u*), 'radial fibres' of Müller.

(*Polyak*, 1941)

4

been the measurement of spectral sensitivities. Such measurements consist of finding out how the amount of light energy, needed to evoke a given constant response, depends on the wavelength of the light.

In human subjects equality of sensation can be used as the criterion for equality of response. For example, the subject can be asked to say when two lights of different wavelengths seem equally bright to him.

With animals similar information can be obtained (though with less precision) by observing their behaviour under controlled conditions. Thus the spectral sensitivity of the South African clawed toad (*Xenopus laevis*) has been measured (DENTON and PIRENNE, 1951) by noting the light intensities below which the animals failed to go into the dark part of their tank, it being a characteristic of Xenopus to seek the shade.

When there is no marked natural phototropism, the animal can sometimes be trained or conditioned—depending on its intelligence—to respond to a light stimulus. Thus GUNTER (1952, 1953) trained cats to raise and pass through a hinged panel which was illuminated by white light of feeble intensity in preference to one which was brightly lit. After their training, the animals were required to make a choice between a panel which was lit by feeble white light and one which was lit by coloured light, the wavelength and intensity of which could be varied. By finding at what intensities the coloured stimuli were indistinguishable (to the cats) from the constant white stimulus, GUNTER was able to obtain a spectral sensitivity curve.

In the above examples the conscious or subconscious equation of sensations is the index for equality of response. But other criteria can sometimes be employed; for example the electric changes occurring in the nervous layers of the retina.

Pre-eminent among workers in this field is the Swedish physiologist RAGNAR GRANIT who used a microelectrode method for studying the changes which occurred in the retina when it was stimulated by light.

In GRANIT'S spectral sensitivity measurements the pre-retinal media were first removed from the eyes in order to allow a microelectrode to be placed in contact with a point on the inner surface of the retina. RUSHTON (1949, 1950) has shown that the electrical effects picked up by the microelectrode had their origin in the large ganglion cells of the retina (Fig. 1.2).

Using these effects as the criterion of response, GRANIT found that the retinae of most animals yielded several sensitivity curves according to the state of retinal adaptation and the position of the microelectrode. Thus although only one type of curve—the 'scotopic dominator'—could be obtained from the dark-adapted retina of a given animal, the same retina, when light-adapted generally showed

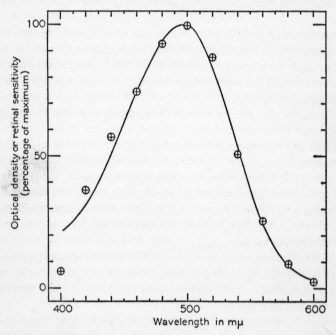

FIG. 1.3. Comparison between the density spectrum of human visual purple (continuous curve) and Crawford's (1949) spectral sensitivity data for the dark-adapted human eye.
(*After Crescitelli and Dartnall*, 1953)

two types—the 'photopic dominator' and several 'modulators,' maximal in different spectral regions. GRANIT considered that the function of the dominators, mechanisms with broad spectral sensitivity curves, is to make 'a large number of wavelengths available for vision'; that of the modulators, mechanisms with much narrower sensitivity curves, the mediation of wavelength discrimination. GRANIT's 'dominator-modulator' theory (1943, 1947) thus suggests in visual terms that both the dark- and light-adapted retina have their

6

specific 'luminosity' mechanisms (the dominators) while the light-adapted retina possesses, in addition, mechanisms (the modulators) which may act as mediators of colour vision.

THE VISUAL PIGMENTS

The chain of events which results when light falls on the retina has its origin in the rod-cone layer. How does this layer respond to light and thus initiate the electrical changes which eventually reach the brain? The first requirement for any of the various mechanisms which might be proposed is that the light shall be absorbed, for it is only so that its energy can be utilized. One would expect to find, therefore, that the rods and cones were associated with light-absorbing substances.

Such is, in fact, the case; coloured substances—the visual pigments—can be extracted from the rod-cone layer of retinae. It is now generally accepted that the spectral regions in which the sensory mechanisms of vision are active are determined by the light-absorbing properties of these substances. Indeed, a few satisfactory correlations have been made. The best-known example is the agreement between the sensitivity curve for the dark-adapted human eye and the absorption spectrum of human 'visual purple.' A comparison of modern data for these is shown in Fig. 1.3.

It is not the purpose of this book to deal with the visual aspects of the visual pigments, however, but to describe their physical and chemical properties and the methods which have been used to determine them.

PREPARATION OF VISUAL PIGMENT SOLUTIONS

The visual pigments are highly photosensitive: if they are exposed to such light as they can absorb, they are destroyed. Consequently, when one is carrying out extraction procedures, it is necessary to work under 'photographic' conditions, i.e. in a dark room lit by non-actinic light. Generally, a deep red safe-light is used. For certain operations, such as removal of the retinae, a more localized illumination may be needed. This can be safely provided by a small torch fitted with Ilford 'monochromatic' filter No. 609, which transmits from 650 mμ to the infra-red.

The first step in the preparation of a visual pigment solution is to dark-adapt the animal. During the darkness period (which need be only an hour or two) the concentration of visual pigment in the retina rises to its maximum value. In some cases this period of dark adaptation is useful for another reason. In fish, birds, most amphibia and some reptiles—but not in mammals—the dark brown granules of the pigment epithelium (Fig. 1.2) move forward on light adaptation and recede again in the dark. Thus in certain light-adapted retinae the outer limbs of the rods and the granules are inextricably mixed. In the dark-adapted condition, however, the retina can be cleanly removed. Movement of the granules is largely conditioned by light, but is also partly dependent on temperature. There is often also a strong diurnal rhythm, and on this account, frog retinae can be more cleanly removed in the evening than in the morning.

Although dark-adaptation of the living animal is advisable, it is not essential. Eyes obtained from a slaughterhouse have been exposed to light and yet from them satisfactory preparations of visual pigments can often be made. Regeneration of the visual pigment does not seem to cease at once on the death of the animal and, if such eyes are kept in darkness for an hour or two, some replenishment occurs. Ideally, the operator should attend the killing and put the eyes immediately into a light-tight box.

REMOVAL OF THE RETINA

After killing the animal the next step is to obtain the retinae. The manner in which this is done depends partly on the size of the eye, and no general rules can be given. With frogs and toads, the animals are first decapitated and the heads washed free from blood. A head is then held in the left hand with the forefinger on the palate and the thumb, in opposition, on top of the head. The forefinger provides a backing to the eye. A blade-point of a sharp pair of scissors is then pressed into the side of the eye at the corneal-scleral junction and a single cut made right across the cornea. By applying gentle pressure with the forefinger, first the lens and then the retina appears through the cut. The retina can then be gently lifted away. The retinae of the frog and indeed of most small animals is surprisingly coherent and is little damaged by this procedure. On placing it in water, for example, it resumes its shape, billowing out into a hemisphere—at the base of which can be seen a small hole where it was torn from its connections to the optic nerve.

A somewhat similar procedure works well with small fish eyes. In these cases, the tapering end of a 10 ml centrifuge tube may be thrust deep into the gullet of the fish until, with some tearing of the tissue, the end of the tube lies behind and between the eyes. In this position, the tube acts as a support for the eyes, as did the forefinger in the case of the frog. By using the tube as a lever, either eye may be made to protrude. A cut is then made across the cornea and the lens and retina pressed through as before.

Larger eyes are first removed from the animal. Thus ox eyes, received from a slaughterhouse, are first cleaned and then cut into posterior and anterior halves by peripheral incisions at about the level of the ora serrata. The anterior half contains the cornea, aqueous humour, iris and lens and is discarded. The posterior half, containing the retina, is full of the jelly-like vitreous humour. This may be spilled out, care being taken not to disturb the retina. With a soft paint brush the retina is then gently coaxed away from the underlying pigment epithelium and heaped up around the optic nerve. The cup is then turned inside-out like a half-orange skin. The retina hangs down from the optic nerve from which it may be snipped away. This procedure may also be used with human eyes.

EXTRACTANTS FOR VISUAL PIGMENTS

The visual pigments, as exemplified by visual purple, can be extracted from retinae by aqueous solutions of certain substances. The first workers used bile salts but in 1931 TANSLEY introduced digitonin, a rare glucoside found in the seeds of the purple foxglove, *digitalis purpurea*. Digitonin, because it is colourless, quickly supplanted the bile salts, and since 1931 has been used in most work. However, it is now possible to obtain certain of the bile salts—for example, sodium cholate and sodium deoxycholate—as colourless powders, and these efficient extractants have the advantage over digitonin of dissolving readily in cold water. Saponin is also effective but the pure-white powder should be used. The yellow powder usually supplied gives a solution which turns brown in a few hours. Certain synthetic substances, in particular cetyltrimethylammonium bromide (CTAB) or chloride (CTAC), are excellent and much cheaper than digitonin. Extractants, such as the soaps, which require alkaline conditions should be avoided as these give opalescent solutions which cannot be clarified by normal centrifuging. To obtain a crystal clear visual pigment preparation the extracting solution should be acid (pH 4–5). After separation of the extract from the retinal debris, it may then be made alkaline, but not before.

9

Digitonin and saponin are usually used in 1–2 per cent concentration, the bile salts and CTAB are satisfactory in 4 per cent concentration.

Mode of action of the extractants. All the extractants have amphipathic properties, that is their molecules are in part water-attracting (hydrophilic) and in part oil-attracting (oleophilic or hydrophobic). Such molecules tend to align themselves at an oil/water interface so that the hydrophilic end is in the water phase and the oleophilic end in the oil phase. This interfacial activity makes them useful in stabilizing oil-in-water or water-in-oil emulsions.

Amphipathic substances may be non-electrolytes, which dissolve in water without producing ions (e.g. digitonin), or they may be electrolytes and dissolve to give a simple inorganic ion and an oppositely-charged amphipathic ion. The amphipathic ion may be negatively charged (e.g. the cholate ion of sodium cholate) or positively charged (e.g. the cetyltrimethylammonium ion of CTAB or CTAC). Visual pigments can be efficiently extracted by representatives of all these types.

The mechanism of extraction is still not completely understood but recently our knowledge has been advanced through an interesting study of an homologous series of positively charged amphipathic ions (BRIDGES, 1955). BRIDGES examined the extracting efficiency of the substances,

$$CH_3-(CH_2)_n-\overset{+}{N}H_3\}\overset{-}{Cl}$$

from $n = 4$ to $n = 15$. He found that the molecular ratio of extractant to visual purple (the conditions of extraction being such that the retinal visual purple was in excess of the extracting agent) varied from *c.* 50,000 in the case of amylammonium chloride ($n = 4$), the least effective substance, to 330 for cetylammonium chloride ($n = 15$), the most effective.

BRIDGES considers that, with these compounds, the positively-charged nitrogen combines electrostatically with the negatively-charged free carboxyl groups of the visual purple protein. This means that the hydrophobic parts of the extractant molecules are oriented outwards to give a complex (Fig. 1.4 (*a*)) which would be insoluble in water. However, a second molecular layer of extractant with like part to like (Fig. 1.4 (*b*)) would reverse this and confer solubility in water. The probability that this is what happens is suggested by the fact that dodecamethylene 1:12-diammonium dichloride ($\{\overset{+}{N}H_3-(CH_2)_{12}-\overset{+}{N}H_3\}\overset{-}{C}l_2$) has an unexpectedly high extraction efficiency. This molecule is hydrophilic at both ends and consequently only a single layer is required (Fig. 1.4 (c)).

BRIDGES' work suggests that negatively-charged amphipathic ions (e.g. cholate, palmityl sulphonate) may function as solubilizers in a converse manner, namely through electrostatic bonding with the positively-charged ammonium groups of the visual purple protein. The mode of action of the non-ionic extractants is unknown.

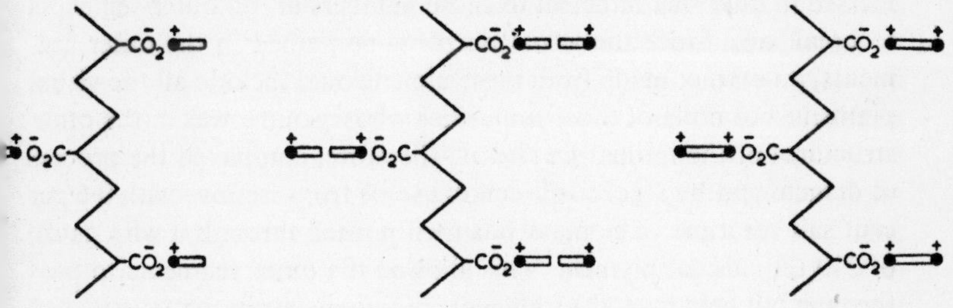

(a) (b) (c)

FIG. 1.4. Diagram to illustrate electrostatic combination between extractant molecules and the carboxyl groups ($-\overset{-}{C}O_2$) of visual purple protein. Filled circles represent the hydrophilic part, and rectangles the hydrophobic part of the extractant molecule.

(*After Bridges*, 1955)

It is an open question whether visual purple—in its native state—is water soluble or not. Water alone will not extract it. But this may be because the visual purple is incorporated in the structure of the rod by electrostatic bonding and hence requires a counter-attraction to take it from its contexture. If visual purple could be freed by physical means, e.g. by the action of ultra-sonic vibrations (SIDMAN, private communication) it would, perhaps, be water-soluble.

EXTRACTION PROCEDURES

When whole retinae are treated with extractants, substances in addition to the visual pigment pass into solution. The principal contaminants are the red haemoglobins and cytochromes, the colourless, water-soluble proteins and the yellow, fat-soluble lipids. Little can be done to purify such an extract. However, by first bathing the

11

retinae in three or four changes of acid buffer solution (pH 4–5) all the blood and most of the other contaminants can be washed away without affecting the visual pigment.

To obtain less-contaminated preparations, involved procedures are necessary. These, for the most part, have been worked out for the visual purple of frog or cattle retinae. There is good reason, however, to suppose that the methods described below have a fairly general application.

In 1937 LYTHGOE noticed that slight disturbance of a retina immersed in fluid was sufficient to cause numbers of rod outer-segments to break off. Since the visual purple is contained in the outer segments, an extract made from these alone would include all the visual pigment, but none of those impurities whose source was in the other structures of the retina. LYTHGOE, therefore, completed the process of detachment by vigorously shaking some frogs' retinae with 0·6 per cent salt solution. The mass was then poured through a wire gauze of 200 threads to the inch. This allowed the outer segments to pass through but held back the fragments of retinal debris. LYTHGOE then centrifuged the filtrate, removed the supernatant salt solution and extracted the residue with digitonin solution. By these means he obtained a visual purple solution which contained less impurities than one made from whole retinae.

SAITO (1938) subsequently described a neater way of obtaining an outer segment concentrate. The retinae are shaken with 35 or 40 per cent sucrose solution. This has a specific gravity nearly the same as that of the outer limbs but less than that of the pigment granules of the epithelium and other parts of the retina. Consequently, when the mixture is centrifuged the outer segments remain in a suspension which can be withdrawn from the unwanted debris. In practice, the aqueous and vitreous humours—a drop of which usually accompanies each retina—often so dilute the sucrose solution that only a poor yield of outer segments is obtained in the first flotation. In this event, and in any case where quantitative yields are sought, the procedure may be repeated by shaking the centrifugate with a fresh portion of sucrose solution.

The suspension is then diluted (e.g. with pH 4·6 buffer solution) to about three times its original volume. The outer segments start to settle out, a process which may be hastened by spinning at 4,000 r.p.m. for 10 minutes or so. The clear supernatant can then be withdrawn and discarded, leaving the compacted mass of outer segments at the

12

bottom of the tube. These, after washing with pH 4·6 buffer, are treated with digitonin or other extractant.

A modified form of SAITO's flotation technique has been used by COLLINS, LOVE and MORTON (1952). The retinae are shaken with saline solution and the mixture filtered through 60-mesh gauze. The filtrate, which contains tissue fragments, blood, melanin, and rod outer segments is transferred to a centrifuge tube. Saturated sucrose solution is then carefully poured down the side of the tube to form a lower layer. A flat-ended glass rod is lowered into the tube and the saline-sucrose interface gently stirred so that a concentration gradient is set up. On then centrifuging the tube, red blood cells, melanin granules, and rod outer segments find their separate density levels and may be cleanly pipetted off. The reader is referred to the paper for practical details and for other useful information on the preparation of visual pigment solutions. KIMURA (1952) has also used a basically similar modification of the flotation technique.

Finally, if the separated outer segments are dried and then treated with light petroleum ether (B.P. 40–60°C) a small amount of yellow pigment (rod lipid) is removed without affecting the visual purple (LYTHGOE, 1937), which can then be extracted in the usual manner.

Visual pigment solutions, adequate for most purposes, however, can be obtained simply by extracting whole retinae after they have been washed in three or four changes of pH 4·6 buffer solution. The treatment with acid buffer removes all blood pigments and renders insoluble a good deal of protein material. Also, the trace of buffer which remains after removal of the washings, ensures that the subsequent extraction is carried out in acid conditions. Extracts made in this way are hardly inferior to those made by SAITO's sugar flotation process. The small amounts of yellow impurities which they contain are quite stable, both thermally and photochemically.

Digitonin extracts of visual purple, buffered at pH 6–10, keep well if stored in darkness in a refrigerator. An extract of frog's retinae, buffered at pH 7·7, was kept by the author for 14 months at 2–3°C without measurable loss of photosensitive pigment.

CHARACTERIZATION OF VISUAL PIGMENTS

ABSORPTION AND DENSITY SPECTRA

The only known way of characterizing the visual pigments is to measure their light-absorbing properties. To do this a sample of an extract is introduced into a glass or quartz optical cell which is bounded by plane, parallel faces (Fig. 1.5). If the intensity of light which enters the first surface, *AA*, of the visual pigment solution is

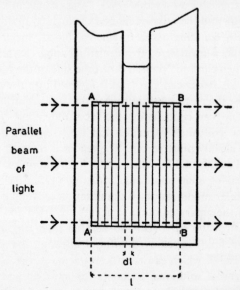

Fig. 1.5. Section of cell used in the measurement of optical densities of solutions. The solution, of thickness *l*, may be regarded as a pile of an infinite number of discs of thickness *dl*.

I_{inc}, and the intensity of light leaving the second surface, *BB*, is I_{trans}, then the light absorbed by the solution is,

$$I_{abs} = I_{inc} - I_{trans}$$

and the percentage of light absorbed by it is,

$$\frac{I_{abs}}{I_{inc}} \times 100 = \frac{I_{inc} - I_{trans}}{I_{inc}} \times 100$$

If the percentage absorption is obtained for light of various wavelengths, absorption spectra can be constructed. Examples are shown in Fig. 1.6 (A) for pure visual purple solutions of different concentrations. In Fig. 1.6 (B) these same curves have been replotted as percentages of their respective maxima. From these it is clear that absorption bands broaden with increasing concentration. This is to be expected for, if a solution absorbs nearly all light at λ_1 and, say,

14

only 25 per cent at λ_2, then doubling the concentration can make little difference to the light absorbed at λ_1, while there is plenty of scope left at λ_2 for further absorption. As the concentration increases, the absorption spectra approach the theoretical limit for infinite concentration which is, of course, 100 per cent absorption of all wavelengths. With decreasing concentration, the absorption spectra (when expressed as percentages of their respective maxima) approach a limiting curve shown by the dotted line in Fig. 1.6 (B).

Absorption spectra thus have the disadvantage that their shape depends on the concentration of the solution. This makes it difficult to compare results from solutions of different strengths.

However, there is another way of expressing results which is free from this objection. Consider the visual pigment solution of depth l (Fig. 1.5) to be made up of an infinite number of thin plates dl. Then, if the intensity of light incident on one of these plates is I, a portion, dI, of the light will be absorbed. If the solution is homogeneous the fraction, dI/I, of light absorbed will be the same for each plate and will depend on the thickness, dl, the concentration c, and a coefficient α_λ, peculiar to the absorption characteristics of the pigment and the wavelength, λ, of the light. Thus,

$$dI/I = \alpha_\lambda . c . dl$$

Integrating this between the limits $I = I_\text{inc}$ and $I = I_\text{trans}$, we have,

$$\log_e I_\text{inc}/I_\text{trans} = \alpha_\lambda . c . l$$

The quantity $\log_e I_\text{inc}/I_\text{trans}$ is the *optical density*. In most work common, not natural, logarithms are used. In these units the optical density is given by,

$$D_\lambda = \log_{10} I_\text{inc}/I_\text{trans} = \alpha_\lambda . c . l/2 \cdot 303$$

In Fig. 1.7 (A) are shown the *density* spectra (i.e. the variation of D_λ with λ) for the same pure visual purple solutions as were illustrated in Fig. 1.6 (A). Density spectra have the advantage over absorption spectra that, when expressed as percentages of their respective maxima (Fig. 1.7 (B)), they become identical, irrespective of the concentration. This readily follows from the definition of optical density, for, if the density D_λ at the wavelength λ is expressed in terms of the density D_max at the maximum, we have,

$$\frac{D_\lambda}{D_\text{max}} = \frac{\alpha_\lambda \, c . l}{\alpha_\text{max} \, c . l} = \frac{\alpha_\lambda}{\alpha_\text{max}}$$

the concentration and optical-path terms cancelling out.

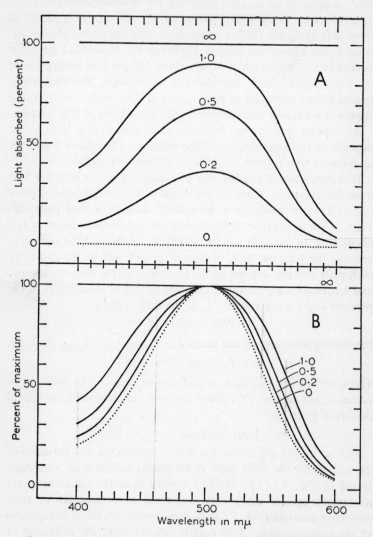

Fig. 1.6. (A) Absorption spectra of visual purple solutions of various concentrations. (B), as (A), but replotted as percentages of their respective maxima.

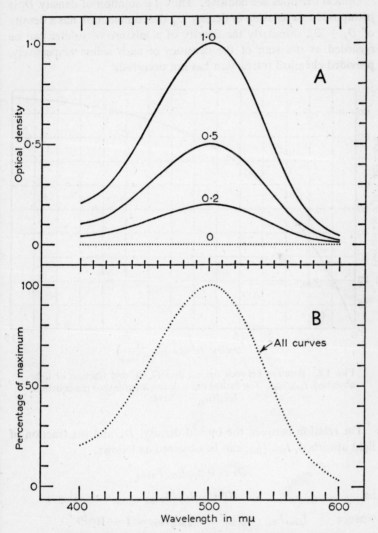

FIG. 1.7. (A) Density spectra of visual purple solutions of various concentrations as in Fig. 1.6. (B), as (A), but replotted as percentages of their respective maxima (all curves the same).

Optical densities are additive. Thus if a solution of density D_1 is juxtaposed to a solution of density D_2, the combination has a density of $D_1 + D_2$. Similarly the density of a mixture of solutes can be regarded as the sum of the densities of each solute respectively, provided chemical interaction has not occurred.

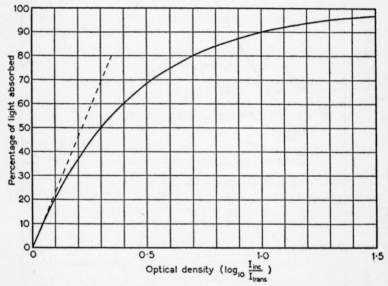

FIG. 1.8. Relation between optical density, D, and fraction of light absorbed, I_{abs}/I_{inc}. The dashed line is drawn according to the equation, $I_{abs}/I_{inc} = 2 \cdot 303D$.

The relation between the optical density, D_λ, and the fraction of light absorbed, I_{abs}/I_{inc}, can be obtained as follows,

$$D_\lambda = \log_{10} I_{inc}/I_{trans}$$

i.e.

$$10^{D_\lambda} = I_{inc}/I_{trans}$$

whence

$$I_{abs}/I_{inc} = (I_{inc} - I_{trans})/I_{inc} = 1 - 10^{-D_\lambda}$$

This relationship is shown graphically in Fig. 8 by the full-line curve.

The expression $1 - 10^{-D_\lambda}$ for the fraction of light absorbed can be expanded into the infinite series

$$2 \cdot 303D_\lambda - \frac{(2 \cdot 303 D_\lambda)^2}{\underline{2}} + \frac{(2 \cdot 303 D_\lambda)^3}{\underline{3}} - \ldots$$

18

If D_λ is small, squared and higher terms can be ignored and the value of the series is then given approximately by the first term, $2 \cdot 303 D_\lambda$ (see straight dashed line tangential to the origin of the curve in Fig. 1.8). Thus in solutions of low optical density ($D_\lambda \gg 0 \cdot 05$) the fraction of light absorbed is nearly a direct measure of the optical density and hence, also, of α_λ, the absorption coefficient. Consequently the absorption spectrum of such a solution (see for example dotted curve in Fig. 1.6) gives the wavelength variation of the absorption coefficient. This characteristic function, approximated by absorption spectra only when the absorption is low, is simply and directly represented when density is plotted against wavelength (see, for example, Fig. 1.7).

The functions obtained by plotting optical density against wavelength are usually called 'absorption' spectra: 'density' spectra would have been a better name. The term absorption spectra is more appropriate to the functions shown in Fig. 1.6, viz. the plots of light *absorbed* vs. wavelength. The use of the name absorption spectra for what are really density spectra sometimes leads to confusion in the literature and, unfortunately, the practice is firmly established.

MEASUREMENT OF DENSITY SPECTRA

In the definition of optical density as $\log_{10} (I_{inc}/I_{trans})$, I_{inc} is the intensity of light entering the front surface of the medium, and I_{trans} that leaving the back surface. It is not possible to measure I_{inc} and I_{trans} directly because of reflections which, in the case of liquids confined in an optical cell, take place at two vessel/air interfaces and at two vessel/liquid interfaces.

This difficulty can be overcome in the following way. A second (reference) optical cell, identical with that containing the solution under test, is filled with solvent alone. The two cells are placed successively in the monochromatic light beam and the intensities of light measured which pass through them. It can be shown (taking first order reflections into account, but neglecting those of the second and higher orders) that D_d, the density of the solute is given by,

$$D_d = D_s - D_r = \log_{10} \frac{I_r}{I_s}.$$

D_s and D_r are the optical densities of the solution and solvent respectively, and I_r and I_s are the intensities of light which leave the

19

rear surface of the 'reference' and 'solution' cells respectively (and hence fall on the light-measuring instrument).

The method gives the density of the solute in the dissolved condition, not the density of the solution as a whole. In a retinal extract, which may contain digitonin, buffer salts and impurities in addition to visual pigments, the absorption due to the digitonin and buffer salts may be eliminated by using in the reference cell an aqueous

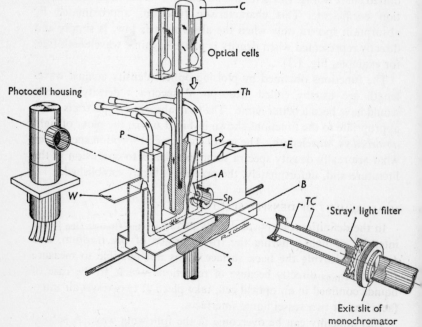

FIG. 1.9. Cell-holder and cells suitable for measuring the optical densities of visual pigment solutions.
(*Dartnall*, 1952)

buffered digitonin solution of the same strength. The density then measured is that of the visual pigment and accompanying impurities of retinal origin.

A typical experimental arrangement for making these measurements is illustrated in Fig. 1.9. The cell holder comprises a movable carrier supported by an outer case. Full movement of the carrier in either direction brings each cell in turn into alignment with the circular apertures A of the outer case, and with the light issuing from a monochromator. Passages drilled in the carrier allow circulation of water from a thermostat, and hence control of the temperature of the solutions during measurement.

In Fig. 1.9 the cell holder is shown in 'exploded' relationship to the monochromator (which delivers light of any wavelength within a certain range), and the light-measuring instrument. Since the visual pigments are photosensitive it is essential to employ light of very feeble intensity. The apparatus must accordingly be of high sensitivity; a photocell of the multiplier type (e.g. RCA 931A) in conjunction with a galvanometer and scale is suitable. With such an arrangement, optical densities can be measured with great precision (e.g. with a standard deviation of 0·0006 for densities within the range 0 to 0·5). On the other hand, a manually controlled apparatus is slow to operate, the time required to traverse the visible spectrum at 10 mμ intervals (each observation checked by a second one) being 40–50 mins.

So far as speed is concerned the Hardy recording photoelectric spectrophotometer has a great advantage. This costly instrument draws the absorption spectrum on paper in about 2 min. It is thus of particular value in studying the transient thermal reactions which follow the photodecomposition of the visual pigments (WALD, 1938, 1939). The instrument would also be useful for investigating the homogeneity of visual pigment preparations (Chapter 6), a laborious undertaking with a manual apparatus.

DIFFERENCE SPECTRA

The density spectrum of an unbleached visual pigment preparation is not wholly characteristic, for it includes the contribution of light-absorbing impurities. If the impurities are stable, and are not affected by exposure to light, the density spectrum of the bleached preparation includes the same contribution from impurities. Consequently, by subtracting one density spectrum from the other, a function which is independent of impurities is obtained. This function, the difference spectrum, is simply the difference between the density spectrum of the visual pigment and that of the product into which it is changed by bleaching.

The value of the difference spectrum for characterizing a visual pigment in the presence of impurities is illustrated by examples in Fig. 1.10. In the upper part of Fig. 1.10 are shown the density spectra, before and after bleaching, of two extracts from the retinae

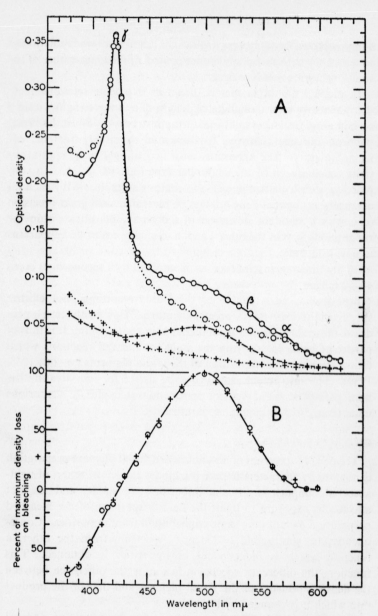

Fig. 1.10. (A) Density spectra, before and after bleaching, of two human visual purple solutions; one (upper curves) heavily contaminated with retinal blood, the other (lower curves) relatively pure. (B) The difference spectra for these two solutions.

of dark-adapted human eyes. One of the extracts, prepared from an unwashed retina, was heavily contaminated with retinal blood. The density spectra consequently show the α-, β- and γ-bands of oxyhaemoglobin. The other extract, prepared from a retina which had been washed in several changes of acid buffer, was free from blood, and contained only a relatively small proportion of yellow impurities. For both extracts, however, the difference spectra (lower part of Fig. 1.10), are in close agreement.

The difference spectrum for human visual purple shows that, on bleaching, density is lost at all wavelengths longer than 425 mμ, and maximally at about 500 mμ. Below 425 mμ the density increases on bleaching owing to the formation of a product with greater absorption than the parent pigment. At 425 mμ, the isosbestic point, the density is unchanged by bleaching.

For the difference spectrum to have a precise significance, it is necessary that the unbleached and bleached states of the solution shall be stable. This requirement imposes some limitations on the experimental conditions (temperature and pH). Control of the pH is also important for the reason that the density spectrum of the product of bleaching depends on the acidity of the solution. Convenient working conditions are pH, 8–9, and temperature, 20°C.

Even if it were easy to prepare absolutely pure solutions of the visual pigments, the difference spectrum would still be an indispensable analytic function. In the examples shown in Fig. 1.10, the solutions were bleached to completion by a single exposure to light. But more information can be obtained when solutions are bleached by a series of exposures. Each instalment of bleaching may be represented as a difference spectrum, and hence compared with any other. In this way the homogeneity of the solution can be tested (see Chapter 6).

REFERENCES

BRIDGES, C. D. B. (1955). *The physical chemistry of visual pigments*. Ph.D. Thesis, London.

COLLINS, F. D., LOVE, R. M. and MORTON, R. A. (1952). Studies in rhodopsin. 4. Preparation of rhodopsin. *Biochem. J.*, **51**, 292–298.

CRAWFORD, B. H. (1949). The scotopic visibility function. *Proc. phys. Soc. B*, **62**, 321–334.

CRESCITELLI, F. and DARTNALL, H. J. A. (1953). Human visual purple. *Nature, Lond.*, **172**, 195–196.

DARTNALL, H. J. A. (1952). Visual pigment 467, a photosensitive pigment present in tench retinae. *J. Physiol.*, **116**, 257–289.

DENTON, E. J. and PIRENNE, M. H. (1951). The spectral sensitivity of the toad *Xenopus laevis*. *J. Physiol.*, **115**, 66P.

GRANIT, R. (1943). A physiological theory of colour perception. *Nature, Lond.*, **151**, 11–14.

GRANIT, R. (1947). *Sensory mechanisms of the retina: with an appendix on electro-retinography*. Cumberlege, London.

GUNTER, R. (1952). The spectral sensitivity of dark-adapted cats. *J. Physiol.*, **118**, 395–404.

GUNTER, R. (1953). The spectral sensitivity of light-adapted cats. *J. Physiol.*, **123**, 409–415.

KIMURA, E. (1952). A new method of separating the outer segments of rods from retinal tissues. *Jap. J. Physiol.*, **3**, 25–28.

LYTHGOE, R. J. (1937). The absorption spectrum of visual purple and of indicator yellow. *J. Physiol.*, **89**, 331–358.

POLYAK, S. L. (1941). *The retina*. University of Chicago Press, Chicago, Illinois.

RUSHTON, W. A. H. (1949). The structure responsible for action potential spikes in the cat's retina. *Nature, Lond.*, **164**, 743–744.

RUSHTON, W. A. H. (1950). Giant ganglion cells in the cat's retina. *J. Physiol.*, **111**, 26P.

SAITO, Z. (1938). Isolierung der stäbchenaussenglieder und spektrale untersuchung des daraus hergestellten sehpurpextraktes. *Tokohu J. exp. Med.*, **32**, 432–446.

TANSLEY, K. (1931). The regeneration of visual purple; its relations to dark adaptation and night blindness. *J. Physiol.*, **71**, 442–458.

WALD, G. (1938). On rhodopsin in solution. *J. gen. Physiol.*, **21**, 795–832.

WALD, G. (1939). The porphyropsin visual system. *J. gen. Physiol.*, **22**, 775–794.

WOLFF, E. (1948). *The anatomy of the eye and orbit*. London, H. K. Lewis & Co. Ltd.

CHAPTER TWO

The Visual Pigments and Their Photoproducts

In 1839 KROHN noted that the rods of Cephalopoda were red but, so far as vertebrates are concerned, the first observations seem to be those of HEINRICH MÜLLER (1851) on the frog. In 1856 MÜLLER wrote 'The substance of rods is often seen to be reddish . . . if it be of sufficient thickness; as for instance when a rod is viewed on end, or several are seen lying together, one over another. This colouring is not uniform all over, but is sometimes stronger, sometimes weaker, often unobservable; and although it appears in eyes which are quite fresh, it may perhaps depend on an imbibition of the colouring matter of blood.'

The first investigators laid stress on the need for fresh retinae to demonstrate the red colour and were oblivious to its relations to light. They had doubts whether the colour was due to a pigment other than blood. Some even doubted whether the colour indicated a pigment at all and thought it possible that the appearances were due to interference phenomena.

In 1876 BOLL discovered that the colour was destroyed by light. Lest the reader be surprised by the apparent tardiness of this observation we quote from KÜHNE (1878) that 'whoever has busied himself with the retina will be reminded by BOLL's discovery (and thereby receive a wholesome admonition of the limits of his own ability), that he has already seen something of the kind before. He will perhaps remember that puzzling blood-clot—which at one moment he saw, or thought he saw, under the retina, and which the next moment disappeared. What he then passed over so lightly was nothing less than the key of the secret, how a nerve can be excited by light. In other words, it was the first fact disclosing the existence of photo-chemical processes in the retina.'

The speed with which the colour of an excised retina disappears depends on the light intensity. In artificial light the change may be quite slow; in bright daylight the colour may vanish almost at once. It is easier, too, to see the colour in some retinae than in others. For example, the frog's retina is deeply coloured; that of the rat, only slightly so.

KÜHNE found that a retina bleached by light regained its colour if left in darkness for some time. But contact of the retina with the pigment epithelium was necessary for this to occur. This was shown by an experiment in which KÜHNE carefully raised about half of a retina from the pigment epithelium and slipped a thin piece of porcelain under the raised portion. The whole was exposed to daylight until it was completely bleached. KÜHNE then removed the porcelain, allowing the raised flap of retina to sink back again. After a few minutes in sodium light (not active in bleaching the retina) he drew the entire retina away to find it uniformly red all over. KÜHNE was so struck by the success of this experiment that he 'was seriously led to try with a piece of tissue paper whether the cup of the eye did not contain a small quantity of red secretion; the morsel of tissue paper, however, came out moist it is true, but quite colourless.'

KÜHNE invented the term 'sehpurpur' for the photo-sensitive retinal pigments. He used this word, which has been translated into 'visual purple,' for all visual pigments, even though, as he himself was the first to observe, their colour ranged, in different species, from red to purple or violet.

According to KÜHNE, when a retina is bleached it becomes successively chamois, orange and yellow in colour before finally becoming colourless. EWALD and KÜHNE (1878) considered that there were three stages in the bleaching: the original pigment visual purple (or rhodopsin); an intermediate pigment which they called visual yellow (or xanthopsin) and, finally, a colourless substance called visual white (or leucopsin). The most effective light for bleaching visual purple was stated to be that of a yellow-green colour but for the conversion of visual yellow to visual white, light of a shorter wavelength, i.e. light strongly absorbed by visual yellow, was necessary.

When an unbleached retina is examined in ultra violet light it shines with a faint bluish fluorescence. After bleaching the retina to the colourless condition, the fluorescence is stronger and of a greenish colour. The new fluorescence is confined to the bacillary layer and, in fact to the outer limbs of the rods as may be demonstrated by brushing these off. When this is done the retina loses its green fluorescence while the brushed-off outer limbs, when massed together, are seen to exhibit it. It was this experiment which lead EWALD and KÜHNE to postulate a final invisible product, visual white or leucopsin, in the bleaching of visual purple.

KÜHNE also found that visual purple could be obtained in solution by treating retinae with bile. He was led to try this because of the solvent action of bile on blood corpuscles, the medulla of nerves and lecithin. 'As to the way in which it works on the rods of the retina, that once seen will never be forgotten. A fresh frog's retina placed in a drop of bile under a cover-slip, immediately breaks out into most wonderful movements, at the edge the rods shoot out like rockets, and where the bile comes in contact with the separated freely moveable outer limbs, these may be seen to curl up like worms, and then suddenly, with a jerk, to stretch out straight again and shoot forward lengthwise; it is just at this moment that the longitudinal striation becomes first visible, then the whole column of the superimposed row of the laminae may be seen, and finally the whole vanishes. It often is as if a roll of coins was shot out of a tube, or like a cartridge of grape shot.'

Solutions of a carmine red colour were prepared by treating frog's retinae with 5 per cent cholate solution. With such preparations KÜHNE satisfied himself that the sequence of colour changes which followed exposure to light was the same as in the intact retina.

Many qualitative experiments were carried out by KÜHNE. The main part of his investigations are described in his monograph 'On the photochemistry of the retina and on visual purple,' an excellent English translation of which was published in 1878. The passages quoted in the present section were taken from this translation and are typical of KÜHNE's vividly descriptive style.

CLASSIFICATION OF THE VISUAL PIGMENTS

In 1896 KÖTTGEN and ABELSDORFF published the results of their quantitative investigations into the light-absorbing properties of the visual pigments. KÜHNE's qualitative observations had already pointed to the occurrence of differently coloured 'visual purples' in different species. KÖTTGEN and ABELSDORFF selected their material from four classes of vertebrates: mammals (4), birds

(1), amphibia (3) and fish (8). The species they used are listed below.

Species studied by Köttgen and Abelsdorff (1896)

Mammals

Ape (*Kalitrichus sabacus*)
Cat
Dog
Rabbit

Birds

Owl (*Strix flammia*)

Amphibians

Common frog (*Rana temporaria*)
Tree frog (*Hyla arborea*)
Toad (*Bombinator bombinus*)

Fishes

Perch (*Perca fluviatilis*)
Pike-perch (*Lucioperca sandra*)
Burbot (*Lota vulgaris*)
Carp (*Cyprinus carpio*)
Tench (*Tinca vulgaris*)
Bream (*Abramis brama*)
Brown trout (*Salmo fario*)
Pike (*Esox lucius*)

Reptiles, the fifth class of vertebrates, were omitted from their investigation since, in agreement with the earlier observations of BOLL and KÜHNE, they found this class to be generally deficient in rods and visual purple, while those members of it which had been reported to possess retinal rods (viz. crocodile, gecko and boa) were not available.

The visual pigment solutions were prepared in red light (an improvement on the sodium light used by KÜHNE) by treating retinae with bile solution. The absorption spectra were measured by a spectrophotometric method. The optical cells containing the retinal extract and the reference solution were situated between the light source and the spectrophotometer (KÖNIG'S). To avoid undue bleaching during the measurement periods, coloured glass filters were interposed between the light source and the cells. In this way the light-sensitive solutions were shielded from all light except that in the spectral region required for measurement.

KÖTTGEN and ABELSDORFF measured the optical densities of their solutions within the spectral range 420–700 mμ. Starting at the red end, measurements were made at 20 mμ intervals, 5 determinations being made at each wavelength. Observations were then repeated in the reverse order, i.e. from blue to red. Comparison of the two sets of data showed that the amount of bleaching during the operation (lasting about 45 min.) was hardly detectable in comparison with the rather large errors of measurement. In any case, any distortion of the density spectrum caused by progressive photodecomposition of the visual pigment was more or less compensated by taking the means of the outward and inward measurements which were, of course, symmetrically arranged in time.

In most of KÖTTGEN and ABELSDORFF'S experiments, difference spectra were directly obtained by measuring the differences between unbleached and bleached samples of the extracts. In the remaining experiments the unbleached extracts were measured versus a bile

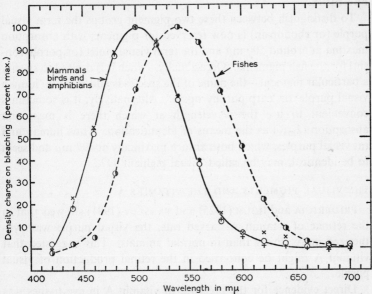

FIG. 2.1. Difference spectra of visual pigments. (O) Mean results for 4 mammals; (×) result for 1 bird; (+) mean results for 3 amphibians; (◑) mean results for 8 fish.
(*Drawn from Köttgen and Abelsdorff's* (1896) *data*)

solution or water, and then again after they had been bleached, the difference spectra being obtained by subtraction. By presenting all their results in the form of difference spectra, KÖTTGEN and ABELS-DORFF eliminated the absorption due to stable impurities, of retinal origin, which had accompanied the visual pigment into solution. It is a pity, however, that they left no record of their measurements versus bile solution or water since these would have indicated the impurity contribution.

The mean difference spectra found for each of the four vertebrate classes are shown, plotted as percentages of their respective maxima, in Fig. 2.1. It is evident that the 'visual purples' are of two kinds.

29

One, found in four mammals, a bird and three amphibians, has maximum absorption in the blue green at about 500 mμ. Human visual purple, as shown by the earlier measurements of KÖNIG (1894) is also in this class. The other kind, found in eight fishes, has maximum absorption in the yellow green (at about 540 mμ), thus accounting for the more violet colour of fish retinae, as first noticed by KÜHNE.

To distinguish between these two pigment groups the term visual purple (or rhodopsin) is now reserved for pigments with absorption maxima at around 500 mμ and the term visual violet (or porphyropsin) for the fish pigments. Occasionally—when it is desired to specify a particular pigment—the name of the species is added, as in 'human visual purple' or 'carp porphyropsin.' Alternatively, it is sometimes convenient to use the wavelength at which there is maximum absorption (λ_{max}) as the means of identification. Thus human and rat visual purples, which both absorb maximally at 497 mμ and seem to be identical, may be called 'visual pigment 497.'

THE VISUAL PIGMENTS AND THE VITAMINS A

FRIDERICIA and HOLM (1925) and TANSLEY (1931) showed that in the retinae of vitamin A-starved rats, the visual purple was synthesized more slowly than in normal animals. This suggested that vitamin A might be concerned in the retinal production of visual purple.

Direct evidence for the presence of vitamin A in eye tissues was first obtained by WALD (1933, 1935a). Vitamin A was identified, in the yellow oil obtained from various eye tissues, (a) by its density spectrum ($\lambda_{max} = 328$ mμ) in chloroform, (b) by the blue colour ($\lambda_{max} = c.\ 620$ mμ) given with the Carr-Price reagent (antimony trichloride), and (c) by the curative property of the oil when fed to rats suffering from vitamin A deficiency. The curative effect of adding retinal tissue to the diet had been noted by previous workers, first by HOLM (1929).

THE RHODOPSIN (VISUAL PURPLE) CYCLE

The intimate relationship between visual purple, vitamin A and a new substance—retinene—was then demonstrated by WALD (1935b, 1936a) in experiments with the retinae of frogs (*Rana esculenta, R. pipiens and R. catesbiana*). WALD found that when dark adapted retinae were extracted in darkness with a homopolar solvent, such as

30

benzine or carbon disulphide, the visual purple was not affected and nothing, save a trace of vitamin A, was extracted. When the retinae were treated with chloroform, however, the visual purple was de-colourized, and the extract contained a yellow pigment ($\lambda_{max} = 385$ mμ) which WALD named 'retinene.' With the Carr-Price reagent, retinene yielded a blue colour ($\lambda_{max} = 664$ mμ).

WALD found that retinene was freely soluble in carbon disulphide or benzine, even though these homopolar solvents would not extract it from dark-adapted retinae. He concluded therefore that the retinene was originally bound to a non-lipoidal complex.

When the retinae of frogs which had been light-adapted were extracted with benzine or chloroform, colourless solutions were obtained, containing appreciable amounts of vitamin A, but no retinene.

The relationship between visual purple, retinene and vitamin A was revealed by further experiments with isolated retinae. On exposing the retinae to bright daylight they changed from a deep red colour to orange. They then slowly faded until, in about an hour they were colourless. WALD found that when retinae were extracted immedi-ately after bleaching, the extracts contained large quantities of retinene, but only a trace of vitamin A. After fading had started, however, the extracts contained less retinene and appreciable amounts of vitamin A. As fading proceeded, the amount of retinene became less and that of the vitamin A, more.

From these and other experiments WALD concluded that vitamin A, retinene and visual purple (rhodopsin) were related in a visual cycle as follows:

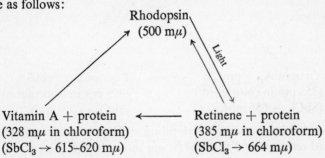

THE PORPHYROPSIN (VISUAL VIOLET) CYCLE

Similar experiments were subsequently carried out with fresh-water fish—and with parallel results. Thus WALD (1937) found that when the retinae of dark-adapted white perch (*Perca flavescens*) were extracted with benzine, the visual pigment (porphyropsin) was not affected. The extract, which was only faintly yellow gave a very pale blue colour ($\lambda_{max} = 696$ mμ) with the Carr-Price reagent. When the retinae were bleached and immediately extracted, however, the extract was deep orange in colour and gave an intense blue colour ($\lambda_{max} = 703$) with antimony trichloride. Bleached and faded retinae yielded a light yellow extract giving an intense blue reaction ($\lambda_{max} = 696$ mμ).

In an examination of fish liver oils, EDISBURY, MORTON and SIMPKINS (1937) reported that they had repeatedly found, on testing with the Carr-Price reagent, a band at 693 mμ in addition to that at 620 mμ (due to vitamin A). They stated 'WALD's discovery that a substance apparently identical with the 693 mμ chromogen can replace the vitamin A of rhodopsin without loss of physiological function runs parallel with the similar replacement in the viscera and liver of the brown trout. It therefore seems desirable provisionally to designate as 'vitamin A$_2$' the 693 mμ chromogen with its characteristic ultra-violet absorption.'

Because of this suggestion, WALD (1939b) proposed the name retinene$_2$ for the orange substance (yielding the 703 mμ band with antimony trichloride) extracted from freshly bleached fish retinae.

Thus WALD proposed a porphyropsin visual cycle with vitamin A$_2$ and retinene$_2$, analogous to that of rhodopsin:

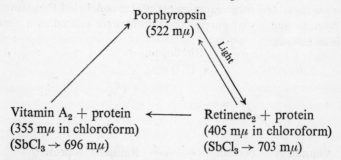

$$\text{Porphyropsin} \atop (522 \text{ m}\mu)$$

Vitamin A$_2$ + protein (355 mμ in chloroform) (SbCl$_3$ → 696 mμ)   ←   Retinene$_2$ + protein (405 mμ in chloroform) (SbCl$_3$ → 703 mμ)

The density spectra of rhodopsin and porphyropsin, and of their related retinenes and vitamins A, are shown in Fig. 2.2.

THE RHODOPSIN-PORPHYROPSIN THEORY

The early investigations of KÖTTGEN and ABELSDORFF (p. 29) had indicated that there were two kinds of visual pigment. One with

λ_{max} at about 500 mμ, found in four mammals, one bird and three amphibians and the other, with λ_{max} at about 540 mμ, found in fish.

The eight species of fish examined by KÖTTGEN and ABELSDORFF were all of the freshwater variety. When WALD (1936b) examined three marine fish—the sea robin (*Prionotus carolinus*) the black sea bass (*Centropristes striatus*) and the scup (*Stenotomus chrysops*), he found that the visual pigments and their inter-relations with vitamin A, and retinene, were the same as in the frog.

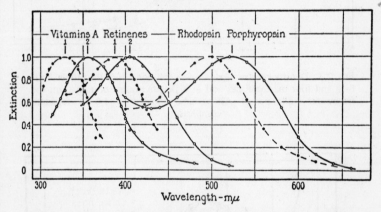

Fig. 2.2. Density spectra of rhodopsin and porphyropsin and of their related retinenes and vitamins A. All maxima equated to 1·0 to facilitate comparison.

(*Wald*, 1939b)

In a later paper (WALD, 1938) these observations were extended to include another marine fish—the killifish (*Fundulus heteroclitus*), two species of frog (*Rana pipiens* and *R. catesbiana*) the rabbit and the rat. The density spectra of visual pigment solutions made from some of these species are shown in Fig. 2.3. The spectra are all approximately the same, having λ_{max} at about 500 mμ (rhodopsin or visual purple, based on retinene and vitamin A).

In the case of freshwater fish WALD (1939b) found that the visual pigment solutions all had λ_{max} at about 522 mμ (porphyropsin, or visual violet, based on retinene$_2$ and vitamin A$_2$). WALD thus confirmed the general result of KÖTTGEN and ABELSDORFF, namely that there are two kinds of visual pigment, but amended the λ_{max} of porphyropsin from 540 mμ to 522 mμ. The density spectra of visual pigment solutions from freshwater fish are shown in Fig. 2.4.

33

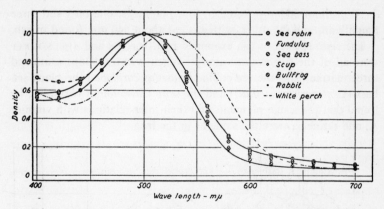

FIG. 2.3. Density spectra of rhodopsin solutions from the rabbit, bull-frog and four marine fishes and of a porphyropsin solution from the freshwater white perch. All maxima equated to 1·0 to facilitate comparison.

(*Wald*, 1938)

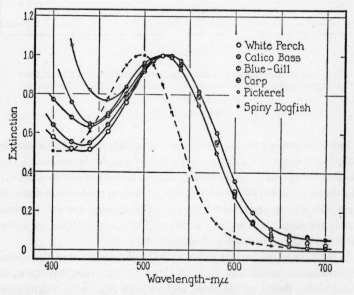

FIG. 2.4. Density spectra of porphyropsin solutions from anadromous and freshwater fish and of a rhodopsin solution from the marine spiny dogfish. All maxima equated to 1·0 to facilitate comparison.

(*Wald*, 1939b)

Since marine fish possessed rhodopsin, and freshwater fish, por-phyropsin, it became of interest to study those intermediate types which spend part of their lives in fresh water and part in sea water. These, the euryhaline fishes are divisible into two groups, the fresh-water spawners (anadromous) and the marine spawners (catadro-mous).

WALD (1939a) investigated the distribution of vitamins A_1 and A_2 in the retinae, other eye tissues and livers of representatives of the various groups. The results he obtained are assembled in the table on p. 36.

The table contains several points of interest. Thus, considering the results from retinae alone, all but one of the permanently marine fish possess only vitamin A_1. The exception is the tautog (*tautoga onitis*) of the family Labridae, the wrasse fishes. Conversely, the retinae of the permanently freshwater fishes contain only vitamin A_2. With the euryhaline fishes, on the other hand, there is generally a mixture of the two vitamins; predominantly vitamin A_2 if the fish is anadromous, i.e. a freshwater spawner, and predominantly vitamin A_1, in the eel, the single example of a marine spawner.

A similar distribution pattern is evident in eye tissues other than the retina. This pattern does not extend to the liver, however, which often contains both vitamins when the retina contains only one. When both vitamins are present in the retina, then both are present also in the liver, but not necessarily in the same proportions; in fact, in the Chinook salmon there is a reversal of the preponderating vitamin in the two locations.

The presence of both vitamins in the retinae of euryhaline fishes, which spawn *either* in the sea *or* in rivers, and the predominance of vitamin A_2 in the tautog—a marine fish—shows that the vitamin A pattern is not absolutely determined by the spawning environments. Likewise, it is not governed by the salinity of the adult environment, for salmonids which have never left fresh water still possess both vitamins; while the eel contains a preponderance of vitamin A_1 after years of living in fresh water, and the alewife a preponderance of A_2 after years in the sea. Again, the pattern is not determined by nutri-tion, for the vegetarian carp has the same pattern as the carnivorous pickerel and calico bass and, conversely, eels which had been caught in the same pond as pickerel and calico bass had reverse patterns.

WALD (1939a) concluded, therefore, that 'the vitamin A configura-tions of both eye and liver are determined by genetic factors.

The proportions of vitamin A_1 and A_2 in fish-eye tissues and livers. The results are expressed in 'colour equivalents' of the Carr-Price test: the extinction at 618 mμ due to vitamin A_1 compared with the extinction at 696 mμ due to vitamin A_2. Each pair of values is scaled to 100. (Wald, 1939a.)

Type	Fish	Retinae		Other eye tissues		Livers	
		A_1	A_2	A_1	A_2	A_1	A_2
Marine	Sea bass	100	0	–	–	–	–
	Scup	100	0	–	–	–	–
	Sea robin	100	0	–	–	–	–
	Sand flounder	100	0	100	0	94	6
	Smooth dogfish	100	0	100	0	–	–
	Spiny dogfish	100	0	100	0	100	0
	Herring	100*	0	100	0	80	20
	Haddock	100*	0	–	–	–	–
	Whiting	100*	0	–	–	–	–
	Tautog	18*	82	–	–	–	–
	Halibut	–	–	–	–	92	8
	Cod	–	–	–	–	100	0
Fresh water	Pickerel	0	100	–	–	0	100
	Calico bass	0	100	0	100	0	100
	Carp	0	100	0	100	65–75	25–35
Anadromous	White perch	0	100	?	?	–	–
	Alewife	0*	100	–	–	19	81
	Chinook salmon	29	71	20	80	75–80	20–25
	Rainbow trout	38	62	30	70	41	59
	Brook trout	35	65	30	70	90	10
Catadromous	Eel	62	38	50	50	99	1

* Pigmented epithelium included.

Presumably these operate through specific enzyme systems which govern the conversion of dietary carotenoids, ultimately of plant origin, into the vitamins A.'

WALD (1941) found that the visual pigment solutions obtained from euryhaline fish had density spectra intermediate between those of rhodopsin and porphyropsin. In Fig. 2.5 the density spectra of visual pigments from various fish illustrate the transition from the rhodopsin system (the permanently marine dogfish) to the porphyropsin system (the anadromous white perch). WALD assumed that the intermediate spectra obtained from euryhaline fish were due to mixtures of rhodopsin and porphyropsin.

From the results of these and other investigations WALD (1949) summarizing the position regarding rod pigments wrote 'true land

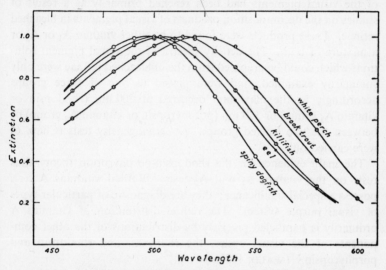

FIG. 2.5. Density spectra of photopigments from various fish. The curves illustrate the hypothesis that the permanently marine dogfish possesses rhodopsin alone, the catadromous eel and killifish predominantly rhodopsin, the anadromous brook trout predominantly and the anadromous white perch exclusively porphyropsin. All maxima equated to 1·0 to facilitate comparison.

(*Wald*, 1941)

and sea vertebrates have the rhodopsin system; true fresh-water vertebrates have porphyropsin; while those equivocal forms which can distribute their lives between fresh water and one of the other environments frequently possess both photopigments mixed or in temporal succession.' In 1953 WALD reiterated his conclusion that 'in the rods of vertebrates there is substantial evidence for the existence of only two visual pigments, rhodopsin and porphyropsin. The distribution of these pigments has been explored to the point at which it begins to seem probable that there are no others.'

AN APPRAISAL OF THE RHODOPSIN-PORPHYROPSIN THEORY

Recent work appears to cast some doubt on the rhodopsin-porphyropsin theory, as epitomized in the last two quotations from WALD. Some of this doubt stems from recent researches by WALD and his colleagues and some from work by the author.

We have seen that WALD'S conclusions regarding the distribution of the visual pigments had been reached primarily as a result of studies on the decomposition products of visual pigments in bleached retinae. These products were found to be either vitamin A_1 or A_2 or a mixture of both. The density spectra of the visual pigment solutions which could be prepared from the unbleached retinae were only summarily examined, and were placed in one of three groups accordingly as the maximum occurred at 500 mμ (rhodopsin or vitamin A_1 group) or 520 mμ (porphyropsin or vitamin A_2 group) or between the two (mixed group). No homogeneity tests (Chap. 6) were carried out.

The main evidence for the rhodopsin-porphyropsin theory thus rests on the vitamin A_1 and A_2 tests. 'Retinal vitamins A . . . possess a special significance; they are diagnostic of particular types of visual purple system. The retinal distribution of vitamins A ordinarily is paralleled precisely by distributions of the other components of the visual cycles, the retinenes, and rhodopsin and porphyropsin.' (WALD, 1939a.)

But it is now known that retinene$_1$ and retinene$_2$, and vitamins A_1 and A_2, can exist in a number of different cis-trans forms, some of which combine with suitable proteins to yield photosensitive pigments of quite distinct properties (see Chapter 5). Nevertheless all five known isomers of retinene$_1$ give an *identical* density spectrum when tested with the Carr-Price reagent. 'If one wishes to have a measure of retinene concentration—and presumably also of vitamin A—that is independent of cis-trans configuration, this is the way to do it' (HUBBARD, GREGERMAN and WALD (1953)).

Thus the Carr-Price reaction can only be used for deciding whether a visual pigment is derived from vitamin A_1 or vitamin A_2; it is useless for deciding which particular isomers of the vitamins are involved.

We are left, therefore, with the density spectra of the visual pigments themselves as the only guide to their identity or otherwise. The presence of varying amounts of yellow impurities in the extracts, however, complicates the interspecies comparison of density spectra, and wide limits were tolerated by WALD when assigning a visual pigment to the rhodopsin or porphyropsin groups (see Figs. 2.3 and 2.4).

The density spectrum of a photometrically pure solution of a visual pigment has a minimum value of about 20 per cent on the blue side of the maximum. The presence of yellow impurities (which absorb with increasing strength towards the short-wave limit of the visible spectrum) results in a raising of this minimum and a displacement of the λ_{max} of the extract to a shorter wavelength.

The purity of an extract can be roughly expressed by the ratio of its optical density at the minimum (D_{min}) to that at the maximum (D_{max}). The purer the extract, the lower is this ratio. In an investigation of carp retinae, CRESCITELLI and DARTNALL (1954) prepared extracts with D_{min}/D_{max} ratios ranging from 0·98 to 0·57, the λ_{max} ranging correspondingly from 500 to 520 mμ. They did this by varying the number of pre-extraction washings and by using different procedures. In Fig. 2.6 the D_{min}/D_{max} ratio is plotted as a function of the λ_{max} of the extracts. Data from SAITO (1938) and WALD (1939b) for carp are also included in the figure.

Rayleigh scattering in a slightly opalescent extract has an effect similar to that of yellow impurities. According to COLLINS and MORTON (1950a) the λ_{max} displacement is 1 mμ when the scattering is such as to raise the D_{min}/D_{max} ratio to between 0·33 and 0·45, 2 mμ if it raises the ratio to 0·45–0·55, and 3 mμ if to 0·55–0·63. These limits are shown in Fig. 2.6 by the vertical bars and they accord with the other data in showing a fairly close correlation between the D_{min}/D_{max} and the λ_{max}.

It is reasonable to suppose that the relationship between the D_{min}/D_{max} ratios and the absorption maxima of carp extracts will hold good for visual pigment extracts made from other fish, provided the same visual pigment is involved or, at least, if its absorption characteristics are not very different from those of visual pigment 523, the carp pigment.

In Fig. 2.6 an inset wavelength scale, calibrated in mμ displacements from the pigment maximum, has been provided. This allows the figure to be used for interpreting the crude extract data of other species. For example, COLLINS and MORTON (1950a) and DARTNALL (1952) both prepared visual pigment solutions from the pike. COLLINS and MORTON's extract had $\lambda_{max} = 525$ mμ and D_{min}/D_{max}

$= 0.86$ while DARTNALL'S had $\lambda_{max} = 530$ mμ and $D_{min}/D_{max} = 0.58$. From Fig. 2.6, D_{min}/D_{max} ratios of 0.86 and 0.58 correspond to λ_{max} displacements of 10 and 3 mμ indicating the closely-agreeing values of 535 and 533 mμ respectively, for the λ_{max} of the pike

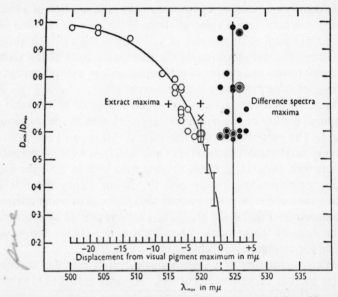

FIG. 2.6. Relation between the 'purity' of retinal extracts (D_{min}/D_{max} ratios) and the λ_{max} illustrated with reference to the carp. O, Crescitelli and Dartnall's data; +, Saito's data; ×, Wald's data; I, Collins and Morton's limits. Note that the λ_{max} of difference spectra (●) are independent of the presence of impurities.

(*Crescitelli and Dartnall*, 1954)

pigment. These, and some further examples, are shown in the table opposite.

The five visual pigment extracts (white perch, calico bass, blue gill, carp and pickerel—see Fig. 2.4) which led WALD (1939) to characterize the pigment 'porphyropsin' had D_{min}/D_{max} ratios ranging from 0.51 to 0.77. The pickerel extract, for example, with $\lambda_{max} = 525$ mμ had $D_{min}/D_{max} = 0.77$. Adding 7 mμ, the displacement correction appropriate to this ratio (Fig. 2.6) we obtain 532 mμ as the λ_{max} for the pickerel pigment. On the other hand WALD'S carp data, after similar correction (see table), yield a λ_{max} of 524 mμ, in good agreement with CRESCITELLI and DARTNALL'S (1954) results for this fish (visual pigment 523).

Thus the porphyropsin group includes pigments with λ_{max} ranging from 524 to 532 mμ. Whether these 'vitamin A$_2$' pigments are single or mixtures is undecided, for WALD did not test their homogeneity (see Chap. 6). Because of these facts it is better to use 'porphyropsin'

Calculation of the λ_{max} of visual pigments from the data of impure extracts.

Fish	Reference	D_{min}/D_{max}	λ_{max} (mμ)	λ_{max} displacement† (mμ)	λ_{max} of visual pigment (mμ)
Carp (*Cyprinus carpio*)	Saito, 1938	0·70 0·70	515 520	5 5	520 525
Carp (*C. carpio*)	Wald, 1939b	0·65	520	4	524
Carp* (*C. carpio*)	Crescitelli and Dartnall, 1954	0·98–0·57	500–520	23–3	523
Perch (*Perca fluviatilis*)	Collins & Morton, 1950a	0·82 0·74 0·83	524 528 520	9 6 9	533 534 529
Pickerel (*Esox reticulatus*)	Wald, 1939b	0·77	525	7	532
Pike (*E. lucius*)	Collins & Morton, 1950a	0·86	525	10	535
Pike* (*E. lucius*)	Dartnall, 1952	0·58	530	3	533

* These extracts have been shown to be homogeneous, i.e. to contain only one photosensitive pigment.
† See Fig. 2.6.

as a generic name for all rod visual pigments based on vitamin A$_2$ rather than as a name for a specific pigment with $\lambda_{max} = 522$ mμ. Similar remarks may be applied to 'rhodopsin.'

THE PHOTOPRODUCTS OF VISUAL PURPLE

KÖTTGEN and ABELSDORFF considered that the effect of light on the visual pigments was to bleach them directly to colourless products. KÜHNE, on the other hand, had stated that the immediate product of bleaching was 'visual yellow' and that this initial product passed to the colourless 'visual white' only as the result of a second reaction.

KÖTTGEN and ABELSDORFF (1896) admitted 'one of us often saw a yellow colour as a transition stage in the process of bleaching—especially in retinae' but they attached little importance to such appearances. The yellow colour could, presumably, have arisen from mere dilution of the visual pigment colour as bleaching proceeded, particularly since the bile solutions used in extraction were faintly yellow.

KÜHNE had stated that the light most effective in converting visual yellow to visual white was of short wavelength. One would expect therefore that visual pigment solutions exposed to such light would bleach to the visual white stage, while those exposed to long-wavelength light would go only to the yellow stage. In fact, however, KÖTTGEN and ABELSDORFF found that difference spectra obtained by bleaching visual pigment solutions were the same whatever the bleaching light (white, yellow or blue). This was a cogent argument against a yellow stage if, as KÜHNE had implied, the conversion of visual yellow to visual white was a photochemical rather than a thermal reaction.

A key to the partial resolution of these differences was provided by GARTEN in 1907. GARTEN remarked that the lights used by KÖTTGEN and ABELSDORFF for bleaching their solutions were weak, and that an intense bleaching light was necessary to reveal a yellow stage in the bleaching process. GARTEN also observed that when a frog's retina was suddenly bleached at − 20°C its colour changed to bright orange, but that on raising the temperature to − 5°C further fading took place. HOLM (1922), from the bleaching of intact retinae, concluded that the formation of visual yellow was dependent on the visual purple being bleached by intense light. He thought that the function of visual yellow was to act as a filter and thus preserve the eye from the effects of high illumination.

In 1929 NAKASHIMA observed that 'visual yellow' was a deeper yellow in acid than in alkaline solutions, while in 1936 CHASE found that 'visual yellow' is an acid-base indicator and thought that the discrepancy between the results of GARTEN (visual yellow formed) and KÖTTGEN and ABELSDORFF (visual yellow not formed) resulted from differences of pH.

The facts were, however, more complex than any of these workers thought and it was not until their observations had been extended and given quantitative expression by LYTHGOE that some understanding was obtained of the sequence of reactions taking place when visual purple is exposed to light. Even to-day, however, these problems are not completely settled.

LYTHGOE (1937) soon recognized that there were two distinct phenomena embraced by the term 'visual yellow.' He divided a solution of frog visual purple into two samples, one of which was cooled in ice and the other warmed to about 30°C. On exposing them both to daylight, the cold solution bleached to a deep vermillion-orange colour, the warm solution to a pale yellow. The chilled solution remained orange for a considerable time at 0°C but, on warming became pale yellow like the other. This simple experiment suggested that by exposure to light, visual purple is first changed into an unstable initial photoproduct ('transient orange') which then fades—at a rate depending on the temperature to a new, and much more stable substance, 'indicator yellow.' For the certain observation of the transient orange stage a low temperature is necessary, though it can easily be seen at room temperature if the visual purple is quickly destroyed by exposure to light of high intensity.

Since, under ordinary conditions, transient orange makes but a fleeting appearance it has passed unnoticed by many workers, particularly those who have relied on the relatively slow measurements of density spectra, rather than on the evidence of their eyes. Such workers have accordingly used the term 'visual yellow' to describe the comparatively stable end product into which transient orange passes—LYTHGOE's indicator yellow.

Indicator yellow, as its name implies is an acid-base indicator. It is a deep chrome yellow colour in acid solution and pale yellow in alkaline solutions. These colour changes are reversible, and either form of indicator yellow can be converted to the other by mere adjustment of the pH.

THE INITIAL PRODUCT OF BLEACHING

Transient orange. The density spectrum of transient orange was measured by LYTHGOE and QUILLIAM in 1938. With their apparatus the measurement of density spectra was a slow process. In order to 'catch' the transient orange, therefore, they carried out the experiments at 3°C. Even at this temperature, however, the rate of fading was very rapid and consequently only a rough estimate could be obtained.

Fig. 2.7 shows the results of one experiment. After measuring the density spectrum of the visual purple solution (V.P.) it was exposed for 3 sec. to a very intense light. Optical density measurements within the wavelength ranges of 460–490 mμ and 395–430 mμ

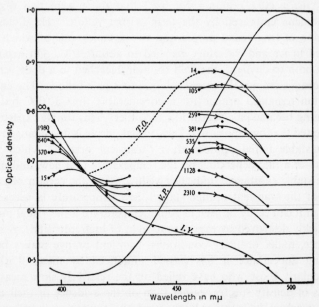

FIG. 2.7. The density spectrum of transient orange (T.O.) in relation to that of the parent (frog) visual purple (V.P.). The numbers against the points give the times (in seconds) at which the readings were taken, and the arrows show the order of taking them. The curve I.Y. was measured when the thermal decomposition of transient orange was complete. 3°C, pH 7·13.

(*Lythgoe and Quilliam*, 1938)

were then made as quickly as possible. The numbers in Fig. 2.7 give the times (seconds from end of exposure) at which the relevant measurements were made. After readings had been repeated for about ¾ hr. the temperature of the solution was raised to *c*. 20°C for 20 min. in order to complete the thermal destruction of the transient orange. The solution was then cooled again and it yielded the curve *IY* in Fig. 2.2. The readings on the curve *TO* in Fig. 2.7 were all taken within 1¼ min. after bleaching and give the approximate density spectrum of transient orange. We now know from the work of COLLINS and MORTON (1950c) that when a cold visual purple solution is bleached to the transient orange stage, and then allowed to stand in darkness, some of the transient orange breaks down to indicator yellow and some takes part in the formation of a photosensitive pigment ('iso-rhodopsin'). (This is well shown in Fig. 2.9.) Thus the curve *IY* in Fig. 2.7 is for a mixture of indicator yellow and 'regenerated' pigment—not a pure indicator yellow curve as LYTHGOE and QUILLIAM supposed.

LYTHGOE and QUILLIAM repeated this experiment over a range of hydrogen ion concentrations (pH 4·9–9·25). They obtained substantially the same results for transient orange, though in markedly acid or alkaline solutions the early changes in the density spectra— following exposure of the solutions—were too rapid for their slow apparatus. LYTHGOE and QUILLIAM estimated the λ_{max} of transient orange to be at 470 mμ. They also found a quantitative relation between the fading of transient orange and the formation of the final product (indicator yellow). This showed that indicator yellow was formed via transient orange and was not, for example, an alternative initial product of the bleaching.

WALD (1938) also obtained essentially similar results for the 'dark process' that followed irradiation of a visual purple solution (prepared from bull frogs). WALD's apparatus, which recorded an absorption spectrum in 2 min., was admirably suited for the study of unstable intermediates, but he lost some of this advantage through working at a high laboratory temperature (26°C). Consequently WALD's 'dark process,' maximal at *c.* 480 mμ, amounted only to some 20 per cent of the visual purple maximum—compared with nearly 90 per cent found by LYTHGOE and QUILLIAM (Fig. 2.7). Thus over 70 per cent of the transient had already faded before WALD had measured the first curve, a minute or two after bleaching.

WALD (1939b) carried out a similar experiment with a solution of porphyropsin (visual violet) prepared from the white perch (*Morone americana*). In the upper part of Fig. 2.8, curve *A* gives the original density spectrum of the solution, curve *B* that after 30 sec. exposure to a bright light and curve *C* that about an hour later, the solution having been kept in darkness meanwhile. The experiment was carried out at room temperature. Consequently, as in the previous experiment, and in spite of the shortness of the exposure time, considerable fading of the initial photoproduct must have occurred before recording of curve *B* was begun. Moreover, since fading continued during the two-minute measurement period, curve *B* is not a true spectrum, the later (short-wave) part of it being nearly the same as curve *C*, which was taken when fading was complete.

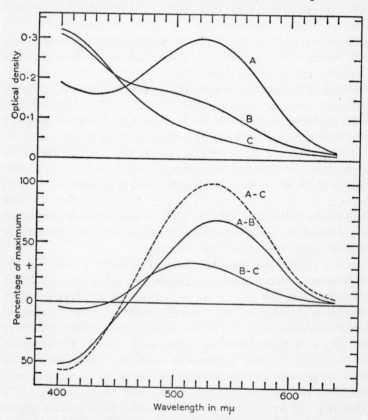

Fig. 2.8. The transient stage in the bleaching of porphyropsin (visual violet). (Neutral extract of white perch retinae.) Curve *A*, density spectrum of a porphyropsin solution before bleaching; curve *B*, ditto after ½ min. exposure to bright light (measurements completed within 2 min.); curve *C*, ditto about 1 hr. later. Lower part of figure shows difference spectra constructed from these curves.

(*Drawn from Wald's* (1939b) *data*)

Owing to the distortion of curve *B*, the difference spectra *A-B* and *B-C* (lower part of Fig. 2.8) must be interpreted with caution. However, we may conclude that to a first approximation curve *B-C* gives

the difference between the initial transient and the final stable product. This curve has a maximum at *c.* 515 mμ (cf. 480 mμ for the
transient orange of visual purple). This experiment provides the
only data we have on the transient of visual violet (porphyropsin).
The overall difference spectrum, *A-C* in Fig. 2.8, gives the changes
that are normally measured, viz. the difference between the density
spectrum of the original visual pigment and that of its final stable
product.

BRODA and GOODEVE (1941) found that a large proportion of
glycerol could be added to solutions of visual purple without effect,
other than that of dilution. By working with solutions consisting of
three volumes of glycerol to one of water, they were able to extend
the range of experiments on visual purple down to − 73°C. At this
temperature the solutions assumed a glass-like consistency and
remained perfectly clear. On exposure to light the solutions
'bleached' to an initial photoproduct (transient orange) which was
quite stable at − 73°C. The density spectrum of the transient orange
was independent of the hydrogen ion concentration between pH 6
and pH 9. On warming the bleached solutions, the transient orange
decomposed to secondary products.

At − 73°C the visual purple density spectrum was narrower and
higher than at room temperature and its maximum was shifted from
505 mμ to 515 mμ. The density spectrum of transient orange at
− 73°C was similarly affected, the maximum being at 510 mμ. The
spectral interval between the maximum at room temperature and
that at − 73°C was thus much greater with transient orange, about
30 mμ, than with visual purple, about 10 mμ. Consequently at low
temperatures the change in colour, when solutions were exposed to
light, was so slight, as to give the visual impression that the visual
purple was photostable.

Lumi- and meta-rhodopsin. Recently, WALD, DURELL and ST.
GEORGE (1950) have described experiments which indicate a further
complexity in the initial stages of bleaching. The first experiment
(see Fig. 2.9) was carried out at low temperatures with a 2:1 glycerol-
water solution of rhodopsin (visual purple). The density spectrum of
this solution was measured at 23°C and at − 45°C. Whilst still at
the low temperature the solution was then exposed to intense white
light until all changes were complete (curve labelled 'lumi-rhodopsin'
in Fig. 2.9). The solution was then warmed to − 15°C in darkness
and, when all changes had ceased, it was cooled again to − 55°C and

its density spectrum measured (meta-rhodopsin). Finally the solution, still in darkness, was warmed to room temperature and its density spectrum measured once more (final product). The final product was a mixture of alkaline indicator yellow (λ_{max} 370 mμ) and regenerated photosensitive pigment (λ_{max} c. 487 mμ).

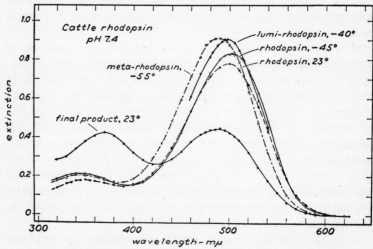

FIG. 2.9. Bleaching of cattle rhodopsin (visual purple) at low temperatures in a glycerol-water mixture. Curves give the density spectra of the preparation after the following treatments. 'Rhodopsin, 23°,' at 23° before bleaching; 'rhodopsin, − 45°,' at − 45° before bleaching; 'lumi-rhodopsin, − 40°,' after complete bleaching at the low temperature; 'meta-rhodopsin, − 55°,' after warming to − 15° in darkness, allowing all changes to complete and then cooling to − 55°; 'final product, 23°,' after allowing it to warm up to room temperature in darkness. All spectra corrected for changes in solvent volume due to changing temperatures.

(*Wald, Durell and St. George* (1950))

In another experiment WALD, DURELL and ST. GEORGE (*ibid.*) showed that the same sequence of reactions took place at room temperature. To record the initial changes, which are normally very transient at room temperature, they took advantage of the fact that in the dry state rhodopsin does not bleach beyond the transient orange stage. They therefore studied the bleaching of rhodopsin in a dried gelatine film. The original density spectrum of their film is shown in Fig. 2.10 ('rhodopsin'). It was then exposed to the very brief illumination of a photoflash lamp and the density spectrum recorded within the first minute thereafter ('lumi-rhodopsin'). The film was kept about an hour in darkness, after which its spectrum was again recorded ('meta-rhodopsin'). Finally, the film was soaked in neutral buffer solution for 10 min., and re-dried. Its density spectrum was then measured ('wetted and re-dried').

The correspondence between the various stages shown in Figs. 2.9 and 2.10 is obvious, and shows that the sequence of changes, first

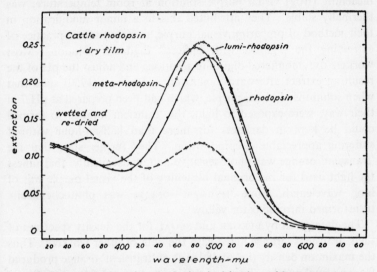

Fig. 2.10. Bleaching of cattle rhodopsin (visual purple) at room temperature in a dry film. Curves give the density spectra of the preparation after the following treatments. 'Rhodopsin,' before bleaching; 'lumi-rhodopsin,' immediately after exposure to a photoflash lamp; 'meta-rhodopsin,' about 1 hr. (in darkness) later; 'wetted and redried,' after soaking in neutral buffer for 10 min. and then redrying—all in darkness.
(*Wald, Durell and St. George* (1950))

revealed at low temperatures can equally well be demonstrated at normal temperatures in the absence of water. From this we may infer that the lumi- and meta-rhodopsin stages do exist in bleached visual purple solutions at ordinary temperatures but that they have a very short life.

It is unlikely that lumi-rhodopsin could survive in solution at 3°C (LYTHGOE and QUILLIAM'S conditions) long enough to have affected the measurements shown in Fig. 2.7. It seems reasonable, therefore, to identify LYTHGOE and QUILLIAM'S transient orange with meta-rhodopsin, rather than with lumi-rhodopsin or with a mixture of the two.

A stable, photosensitive form of transient orange. Before leaving the subject of the initial photoproduct of visual purple, mention should be made of some singular observations by BERGER and SEGAL (SEGAL, 1950; BERGER and SEGAL, 1950a, b). These authors reported that in their experiments the 'transient' orange, formed by bleaching (frog) visual purple solution at room temperature, was thermally stable. They attributed this to a minor modification in their method of preparing visual purple, namely to their practice of extracting the pigment with buffered digitonin solution. Most workers use unbuffered digitonin solutions and adjust the pH of the resulting extract afterwards. BERGER and SEGAL (1950) state that when solutions of visual purple, which had been prepared at pH 7 in their way, were exposed to light, the 'transient' orange so formed could be kept in darkness for more than half-an-hour without suffering appreciable decomposition. They further state that the 'transient' orange was photosensitive and, consequently, that unless the light used for the original bleaching of the visual purple was of long wavelength, some 'transient' orange was photochemically transformed into indicator yellow.

The data given by BERGER and SEGAL for the density spectrum of their 'transient' orange agree with the data of other workers. Thus the maximum density (i.e. at 480 mμ) of 'transient' orange produced from a visual purple solution of maximum density 1·0 (i.e. at 500 mμ) was 0·8 (cf. Figs. 2.7 and 2.10). In particular their data agree well with the density spectrum of meta-rhodopsin, if allowance is made for the fact that their solutions were contaminated with yellow impurities. There is little doubt that the substance they describe is closely related to, if not identical with transient orange. It is the more surprising, therefore, that the properties of their initial photoproduct differ so markedly, viz. in thermal stability and in lightsensitivity, from those accorded to transient orange by other workers. Transient orange is certainly not light-sensitive at very low temperatures, nor when in a dry film, but this may be because water is necessary for the photochemical (as for the thermal) degradation to indicator yellow. Unfortunately, LYTHGOE and QUILLIAM'S experiments in fluid solution at 3°C give no information on the lightsensitivity (if any) of transient orange when in contact with water, for these authors studied the decomposition only in darkness (Fig. 2.7).

BERGER and SEGAL'S experiments recall the old 'visual yellow' controversy. EWALD and KÜHNE reported that 'visual yellow' was photosensitive, a finding which KÖTTGEN and ABELSDORFF could not confirm, because they obtained the same difference spectrum irrespective of whether they bleached visual purple solutions with long- or with short-wave light (p. 42). May it not be that in EWALD and KÜHNE'S experiments the 'transient' orange was thermally stable and photosensitive (as in BERGER and SEGAL'S experiments); while in

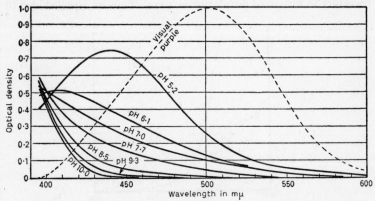

Fig. 2.11. Variation of the density spectrum of indicator yellow with hydrogen ion concentration. The density spectrum of the parent (frog) visual purple is shown by the dotted curve.

(*Lythgoe*, 1937)

KÖTTGEN and ABELSDORFF'S, as in most other workers' experience, the transient orange thermally decomposed to indicator yellow with such rapidity that any light-sensitiveness it may have possessed was overlooked? Further work is clearly required to elucidate these points.

THE FINAL PRODUCTS OF BLEACHING

Under ordinary experimental conditions, the initial products obtained by bleaching visual purple in solution are rapidly transformed into indicator yellow. Indicator yellow is an acid-base indicator, being deep chrome yellow in acid, and pale yellow in alkaline solutions. The reactions of this relatively stable substance were first clearly characterized by LYTHGOE (1937).

LYTHGOE'S measurements of the density spectra of indicator yellow solutions at various acidities within the range pH 5·2–10·0 are shown in Fig. 2.11. The density spectrum of the parent visual purple, which LYTHGOE found to be unaffected by pH, is also shown for comparison.

LYTHGOE conjectured that the density spectrum of pure visual purple approached close to the zero axis at wavelengths shorter than 400 mμ (Fig. 2.11). We now know, however, that the density of pure visual purple at 400 mμ is fully 20 per cent of that at the maximum. LYTHGOE's solutions were, in fact, much more nearly pure than he supposed. The impurity 'corrections' which, at the time, he thought necessary to his visual purple curves were, of course, applied also to

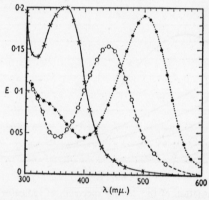

Fig. 2.12. Density spectra of acid and alkaline indicator yellow and of the parent (frog) visual purple. ●, visual purple; ○, indicator yellow in acid solution; ×, indicator yellow in alkaline solution.

(*Collins and Morton* (1950b))

the indicator yellow curves. Consequently, they too are uniformly in error at the shorter wavelengths. Nevertheless the results in Fig. 2.11 clearly show the dependence on pH of the density spectrum. In acid solution (pH 5·2) the indicator yellow maximum is at *c.* 440 mμ while in alkaline solution it shifts into the ultra-violet, beyond the reach of LYTHGOE's apparatus. At *c.* 400 mμ, the indicator yellow curves all have approximately the same ordinate value. It is probable that were it not for the fading of indicator yellow at some pH's, there would have been a true isosbestic point at *c.* 400 mμ. This suggests that indicator yellow exists in two forms and that the curves in Fig. 2.11 represent mixtures of these in different proportions, depending on the pH.

The full density spectra of the two forms of indicator yellow in relation to the spectrum of the original visual purple solution are shown in Fig. 2.12. These measurements, by COLLINS and MORTON (1950b), extend to the ultra-violet and show that the maximum of the alkaline indicator yellow curve is at *c*. 365 mμ and confirm that it is isosbestic at *c*. 400 mμ with the acid curve.

LYTHGOE (1937) found that indicator yellow was stable between pH 10·0 and pH 6·1 but that outside this range it faded, particularly in strongly acid solutions. In 1948, BLISS showed that in acid solution (pH < 7) indicator yellow (λ_{max} 440 mμ) decomposed in a few hours into retinene (λ_{max} 385 mμ) and protein. Retinene, a substance soluble in fat solvents, was first described by WALD (see p. 30) and is the chromophore of indicator yellow. Indicator yellow, like visual purple, is a chromoprotein, i.e. a protein associated with one or more light-absorbing molecular groups called chromophores.

BLISS (1948) showed also that in conditions where acid indicator yellow and retinene were produced, these substances underwent a further chemical change—if the solutions were fresh—to form the colourless vitamin A ($\lambda_{max} = 328$ mμ). BLISS found that this final reaction, which was maximal at pH 6·7 and which did not occur below pH 5·5 nor above pH 8, was probably due to an enzymic factor, present only in fresh solutions, i.e. solutions not more than two hours old.

SUMMARY

The sequence of reactions which may follow exposure of visual purple to light is set out in the scheme on p. 54.

Iso-rhodopsin, which has $\lambda_{max} = 487$ mμ when 'regenerated' in cattle or rat rhodopsin (497 mμ) solutions, and $\lambda_{max} = 493$ mμ when 'regenerated' in frog rhodopsin (502 mμ) solutions (COLLINS and MORTON, 1950c) is shown (because of WALD, DURELL and ST. GEORGE'S experiments) as being produced wholly from meta-rhodopsin (cf. Figs. 2.10 and 2.11). If, in addition, the original rhodopsin can be regenerated from lumi-rhodopsin—a point on which we have no information—then the fact that iso-rhodopsin and rhodopsin are cis-trans isomers suggests that the thermal change of lumi- into meta-rhodopsin is an isomerization process (see Chapter 4, p. 124).

It is not certain whether the enzymic conversion of indicator yellow to vitamin A proceeds directly or *via* retinene. On the whole the evidence (BLISS, 1948) suggests a direct conversion as shown in the scheme.

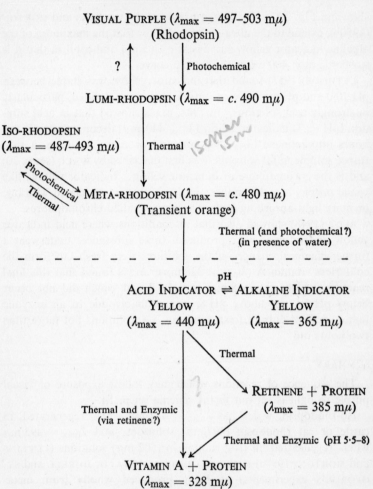

VISUAL PURPLE ($\lambda_{max} = 497\text{--}503$ mμ)
(Rhodopsin)

? | Photochemical

LUMI-RHODOPSIN ($\lambda_{max} = c.\ 490$ mμ)

ISO-RHODOPSIN
($\lambda_{max} = 487\text{--}493$ mμ) | Thermal | *Isomerism*

Photochemical
Thermal ➔ META-RHODOPSIN ($\lambda_{max} = c.\ 480$ mμ)
(Transient orange)

Thermal (and photochemical?)
(in presence of water)

- - - - - - - - - - - - - - - - -

pH
ACID INDICATOR ⇌ ALKALINE INDICATOR
YELLOW   YELLOW
($\lambda_{max} = 440$ mμ)   ($\lambda_{max} = 365$ mμ)

Thermal

RETINENE + PROTEIN
($\lambda_{max} = 385$ mμ)

Thermal and Enzymic
(via retinene?)

Thermal and Enzymic (pH 5·5–8)

VITAMIN A + PROTEIN
($\lambda_{max} = 328$ mμ)

*Scheme showing the products which may be formed when
visual purple is bleached*

The scheme, which embodies the work of a number of authors, enables us to forecast the products of bleaching of visual purple under a wide variety of conditions.

At very low temperatures, or in the dry state, the bleaching of visual purple proceeds only as far as lumi- or meta-rhodopsin and the regeneration of rhodopsin or of iso-rhodopsin either do not occur or are immeasurably slow.

In solution at ordinary temperatures the rates of thermal decomposition of lumi- into meta-rhodopsin and of the latter into acid indicator yellow are very fast. But the regenerative reactions are also fast. Consequently, if a solution of visual purple is bleached by exposing it to an intense light for a very short time, i.e. a time commensurate with the lives of lumi- and meta-rhodopsin, then some regenerated rhodopsin and iso-rhodopsin can be expected in the bleached solution. If, on the other hand, the exposure is prolonged (say ten minutes or more) such regenerated photo-pigments are 're-bleached' while second, third and higher order regenerations become successively less because of the continual 'drainage' to acid indicator yellow. Thus, following a prolonged exposure to light, solutions can contain only those products shown below the horizontal line in the scheme. In what follows we shall assume that such is the case.

The final state of an irradiated preparation of visual purple depends on the conditions, e.g. on the freshness of the preparation and (when the preparation is a solution) on the pH. If a neutral, freshly-made solution is bleached it will slowly fade after the exposure period, sometimes to a colourless condition in which only vitamin A is present. If, however, another sample of the same solution is allowed to age for two or three hours, or alternatively, if in the preparation of the solution the retinae were washed with alum, then the enzyme which catalyses the conversion of indicator yellow and retinene to vitamin A is destroyed and consequently, the neutral solution, after bleaching, contains only retinene and, perhaps, some indicator yellow. ARDEN (1954) found that sucrose *suspensions* of the retinal rods of the frog (which contain visual purple) behaved in a similar way. Thus fresh suspensions bleached to vitamin A, whereas aged suspensions bleached to retinene or, perhaps, indicator yellow. With suspensions, however, the ageing process takes several days, due no doubt, to the protection afforded to the enzyme in its natural environment inside the rod.

If an alkaline (pH 8–10) solution of visual purple is bleached there is a rapid and almost quantitative conversion to the stable, alkaline form of indicator yellow. A slow 'leakage' to retinene via acid indicator yellow may occur, but this makes little difference to the spectrophotometric properties of the bleached solution since the density spectra of retinene and of alkaline indicator yellow are not very different.

All visual pigments so far examined appear to behave on bleaching in an analogous manner to visual purple. It is fortunate that the alkaline conditions, which favour stability of the visual pigment, favour also the stability of the product. Consequently, in alkaline conditions (pH 8–10) difference spectra can be reproduced with precision. Some examples are shown in Fig. 2.13.

Another advantage of alkaline conditions is that the pH-dependent

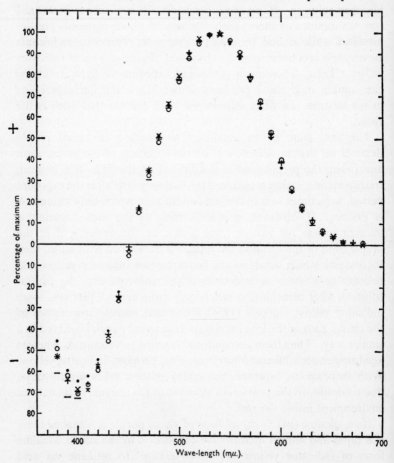

FIG. 2.13. Difference spectra of a visual pigment present in retinal extracts of the tench. pH 8·6, temperature 20·0°C. The symbols indicate the results of five independent determinations. All maxima equated to 100 to facilitate comparison.

(*Dartnall*, 1952)

56

absorption band of the product is then located farthest from the band of the parent pigment. The 'overlap' is minimal and consequently the upper and lower portions of the difference spectrum (Fig. 2.13) are at their nearest approximation to the true density spectra of parent and product respectively. The λ_{max} of an 'alkaline' difference spectrum is displaced not more than 2 or 3 mμ above that for the pure visual pigment (cf. Fig. 2.6).

REFERENCES

ARDEN, G. B. (1954). The dark reactions in visual cell suspensions. *J. Physiol.*, **123**, 386–395.

BERGER, P. and SEGAL, J. (1950a). Le spectre d'absorption de l'orangé transitoire rétinien. *C.R. Soc. biol.*, **144**, 478–479.

BERGER, P. and SEGAL, J. (1950b). La photolyse fractionnée du pourpre rétinien. *Comp. rend.*, **230**, 1903–1905.

BLISS, A. F. (1948). The mechanism of retinal vitamin A formation. *J. biol. Chem.*, **172**, 165–178.

BOLL, F. (1876). Zur Anatomie und Physiologie der Retina. *Monatsber. Akad. Wiss. Berlin*, 783–787.

BRODA, E. E. and GOODEVE, C. F. (1941). The behaviour of visual purple at low temperature. *Proc. roy. Soc. A.*, **179**, 151–159.

CHASE, A. M. (1936). Anomalies in the absorption spectrum and bleaching kinetics of visual purple. *J. gen. Physiol.*, **19**, 577–599.

COLLINS, F. D. and MORTON, R. A. (1950a). Studies on rhodopsin. 1. Methods of extraction and the absorption spectrum. *Biochem. J.*, **47**, 3–10.

COLLINS, F. D. and MORTON, R. A. (1950b). Studies on rhodopsin. 2. Indicator yellow. *Biochem. J.*, **47**, 10–17.

COLLINS, F. D. and MORTON, R. A. (1950c). Studies in rhodopsin. 3. Rhodopsin and transient orange. *Biochem. J.*, **47**, 18–24.

CRESCITELLI, F. and DARTNALL, H. J. A. (1954). A photosensitive pigment of the carp retina. *J. Physiol.*, **125**, 607–627.

DARTNALL, H. J. A. (1952). Visual pigment 467, a photosensitive pigment present in tench retinae. *J. Physiol.*, **116**, 257–289.

EDISBURY, J. R., MORTON, R. A. and SIMPKINS, G. W. (1937). A possible vitamin A_2. *Nature, Lond.*, **140**, 234.

EWALD, A. and KÜHNE, W. (1878). Untersuchungen über den Sehpurpur. *Unters. physiol. Inst. Heidelberg.*, **1**, 139–218, 248–290, 370–455.

FRIDERICIA, L. S. and HOLM, E. (1925). Experimental contribution to the study of the relation between night blindness and malnutrition. Influence of deficiency of fat-soluble A-vitamin in the diet on the visual purple in the eyes of rats. *Am. J. Physiol.*, **73**, 63–78.

GARTEN, S. (1907). Die Veränderungen der Netzhaut durch Licht. *Handb. d. ges. Augenheilk.*, **3**, Chap. 12, 1–250.

HOLM, E. (1922). Sur la décoloration du pourpre visuel. *C.R. Soc. Biol.*, **87**, 465–466.

HOLM, E. (1929). Paavisning af A-vitamin i retina. *Hospitalstidende*, **72**, 139–152.

HUBBARD, R., GREGERMAN, R. I. and WALD, G. (1953). Geometrical isomers of retinene. *J. gen. Physiol.*, **36**, 415–429.

KÖNIG, A. (1894). Über den menschlichen Sehpurpur und seine Bedeutung für das Sehen. *S.B. Preuss. Akad. Wiss.*, **30**, 577–598.

KÖTTGEN, E. and ABELSDORFF, G. (1896). Absorption und Zersetzung des Sehpurpurs bei den Wirbeltieren. *Z. Psychol. Physiol. Sinnesorg.*, **12**, 161–184.

KROHN, A. (1839). Cited by Kühne (1878). Printed in *Nova Acta Acad. Caesar. Leopold.-Carol.* (1842), 11, 1. (Nachträgliche Beobachtung über den Bau des Auges der Cephalopoden.)

KÜHNE, W. (1878). *On the photochemistry of the retina and on visual purple.* Ed. with notes by Michael Foster. London: Macmillan & Co.

LYTHGOE, R. J. (1937). The absorption spectra of visual purple and of indicator yellow. *J. Physiol.*, **89**, 331–358.

LYTHGOE, R. J. and QUILLIAM, J. P. (1938). The relation of transient orange to visual purple and indicator yellow. *J. Physiol.*, **94**, 399–410.

MÜLLER, H. (1851). Zur Histologie der Netzhaut. *Z.f. Wiss. Zoologie.*, **3**, 234–237.

MÜLLER, H. (1856). Anatomisch-physiologische Untersuchungen über die Netzhaut bei Menschen und Wirbeltieren. *Z.f. Wiss. Zoologie.*, **8**, 1–122.

NAKASHIMA, M. (1929). Beitraege zur Kenntnis des Sehpurpurs. *Extrait du Compt. rend. XIII Conc. Ophthal. Amsterdam*, **1**, 317.

SAITO, Z. (1938). Isolierung der Stäbchenaussenglieder und spektrale Untersuchung des daraus hergestellten Sehpurpurextraktes. *Tohoku J. exp. Med.*, **32**, 432–446.

SEGAL, J. (1950). La photolyse de l'orangé transitoire rétinien. *C.R. Soc. Biol.*, **144**, 403–404.

TANSLEY, K. (1931). The regeneration of visual purple; its relations to dark adaptation and night blindness. *J. Physiol.*, **71**, 442–458.

WALD, G. (1933). Vitamin A in the retina. *Nature, Lond.*, **132**, 316–317.

WALD, G. (1935a). Vitamin A in eye tissues. *J. gen. Physiol.*, **18**, 905–915.

WALD, G. (1935b). Carotenoids and the visual cycle. *J. gen. Physiol.*, **19**, 351–371.

WALD, G. (1936a). Pigments of the retina. I: The bull frog. *J. gen. Physiol.*, **19**, 781–795.

WALD, G. (1936b). Pigments of the retina. II: Sea robin, sea bass and scup. *J. gen. Physiol.*, **20**, 45–56.

WALD, G. (1937). Visual purple system in fresh-water fishes. *Nature, Lond.*, **139**, 1017–1018.

WALD, G. (1938). On rhodopsin in solution. *J. gen. Physiol.*, **21**, 795–832.

WALD, G. (1939a). On the distribution of vitamins A_1 and A_2. *J. gen. Physiol.*, **22**, 391–415.

WALD, G. (1939b). The porphyropsin visual system. *J. gen. Physiol.*, **22**, 775–794.

WALD, G. (1941). The visual systems of euryhaline fishes. *J. gen. Physiol.*, **25**, 235–245.

WALD, G. (1949). The photochemistry of vision. *Documenta Ophthal.*, **3**, 94–134.

WALD, G. (1953). The biochemistry of vision. *Ann. Rev. Biochem.*, **22**, 497–526.

WALD, G., DURELL, J. and ST. GEORGE, R. C. C. (1950). The light reaction in the bleaching of rhodopsin. *Science*, **111**, 179–181.

CHAPTER THREE

The Physical Chemistry of Visual Purple

---

1. PHOTOCHEMISTRY

In 1904 TRENDELENBURG measured the relative efficiency of different parts of the spectrum of a Nernst lamp in bleaching visual purple solutions. TRENDELENBURG did not allow for the energy distribution in his Nernst lamp spectrum but, instead, compared the results with the relative sensitivity of human vision (in the dark adapted state) when determined with the same arrangement of apparatus. Good agreement was obtained between the 'bleaching factors' and the 'twilight factors' (relative scotopic sensitivities). In 1911 TRENDELENBURG concluded that the bleaching of visual purple was independent of wavelength, if due allowance was made for the light actually absorbed by the solutions; and in the same year this was confirmed by HENRI and LARGUIER DES BANCELS who showed that when TRENDELENBURG'S original 'bleaching factors' were corrected for energy distribution they agreed approximately with KÖNIG'S (1894) difference spectrum for visual purple.

Further studies of the bleaching kinetics of visual purple were made by HECHT (1920, 1921, 1924). His approach to the problem was direct and simple though, unlike TRENDELENBURG, he used only 'white' light for bleaching. For the bleaching experiments, the visual purple (extracted from frogs' retinae with 3–4 per cent bile salts solution) was transferred to small test tubes about 50 mm long and of 2 mm inside diameter. About 0·1 ml of solution was put into each tube, the length of the liquid column being adjusted to 35 ± 0·2 mm. Concentrations were estimated by comparing the depth of colour, when the tube was viewed end on, with that of standards.

The standards were prepared by making mixtures of an unbleached and bleached visual purple solution. The first consisted of 20 drops of the unbleached solution alone, the second of 18 drops of unbleached with 2 drops of bleached solution and so on to the last, which was unbleached solution alone. The 11 standards so prepared were pipetted into similar tubes to those used in the bleaching experiments and were protected from light by black rubber tubing. In the colorimetric comparisons the experimental solution was similarly jacketted. The matching was done by the light of a 0·04 candle power artificial daylight lamp having a uniform circular surface of 30 mm diameter. This matching light was used only momentarily.

The experimental tube, arranged as in Fig. 3.1, was exposed to light of known intensity, the tube being rotated by hand at roughly 10 r.p.m. by means of the glass rod. After a certain interval the tube was removed from the bleaching light for comparison with the standards, after which it was returned for further bleaching. Concentrations were estimated to the nearest 5 per cent, i.e. to half the difference between standards. HECHT (1920) found that the variation of concentration of visual purple with time of exposure could be expressed by the equation for a monomolecular reaction, namely

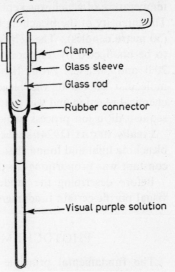

Fig. 3.1. Hecht's experimental arrangement for bleaching visual purple solutions.
(*After Hecht*, 1920)

$$k = \frac{1}{t} \log_{10} \frac{a}{a - x}$$

where a was the initial concentration of the solution (100 per cent) and x the concentration after the time t (minutes).

A further series of experiments was carried out in which the curve of concentration against time was obtained by exposing a number of exactly similar solutions for increasing intervals. In this way each solution was brought to a stage of decomposition by a continuous exposure as opposed to a series of intermittent exposures of the same total duration. No difference was found between the curves obtained in this way and those obtained by the intermittent exposure method.

This indicated that there was no induction or after-effect associated with the bleaching process.

In a second investigation (HECHT, 1921), the effect of temperature was examined. The same technique was used except that the small tubes were immersed in a cylindrical glass vessel filled with water, the temperature of which was kept constant to 1°C by suitable additions. The intensity of the bleaching light was the same for all experiments (50 metre candles). The velocity constants (k) obtained were found to be unaffected by temperature, measurements being made at 5·2, 20·0 and 36·1°C. From this HECHT concluded that the monomolecular course of the bleaching represented the actual photochemical reaction and was not, for example, a measure of some subsequent diffusion process (which would be temperature-dependent).

Finally HECHT (1924) studied the effect of intensity of the white bleaching light and found that, other things being equal, the velocity constant was proportional to the light intensity.

Before describing the modern work on the photochemistry of visual purple certain fundamental concepts may be reviewed.

PHOTOCHEMICAL PRINCIPLES

The fundamental principle of photochemistry is the law, put forward independently by von Grotthuss in 1817 and by Draper in 1841 and verified innumerable times since, that only light which is *absorbed* can cause a photochemical change. Light which is not absorbed can have no effect; though it is sometimes possible for light absorbed by one molecular species to cause change in another, in intimate contact with it, by a process of energy-transfer known as photosensitization. Visual purple itself, in certain circumstances will act as a photosensitizer. Thus KÖGEL (1929) found that Perutz lantern plates which had been converted to AgI by means of the Renwick iodide-sulphite-thiosulphite solution were increased in general sensitivity, and more especially in the green and orange, by bathing them in a 2 per cent sodium glycocholate extract of visual purple. The sensitization conferred diminished rapidly, however, and had disappeared in 24 hours. In this instance the energy at longer wavelengths, normally unabsorbed by the AgI emulsion, was made available to it by the mediation of visual purple. In general, however, the molecular species which absorbs the energy is the one in which the photochemical changes occur.

The particular locality in a molecule where absorption takes place is known as the chromophore. When a beam of light passes through a substance, a part is absorbed and the rest transmitted. On the quantum theory, the energy in the beam is more like the energy of a hailstorm than that of a waterfall in that it consists of a vast number of discrete quanta. If, after passing through a substance the intensity of a light-beam is found to have been weakened to 50 per cent (say) of its original value, this means that one half of the quanta were wholly absorbed by the chromophores of the substance and that the other half emerged completely unscathed.

Photochemical reactions can be regarded as taking place in two stages; the primary process and the secondary process. According to the Stark-Einstein equivalence law, the primary process is the absorption of a single quantum by an individual chromophore. As a result the molecule is raised to a higher electronic level which may be either stable, or unstable and cause dissociation of the molecule. From the standpoint of the primary process every interaction between radiant energy and matter has a quantum efficiency of unity.

$$\left(\text{Quantum efficiency} = \frac{\text{Number of chromophores affected}}{\text{Number of quanta absorbed}}\right)$$

The overall quantum efficiency, however (as measured by some permanent change), depends on the secondary process, namely, the chemical consequences of the original activation. For example an excited molecule may lose all or some of its extra energy by fluorescing or by suffering deactivating collisions with other molecules. In the former case at least some of the absorbed energy is re-radiated, usually as light of longer wavelength (i.e. in smaller quanta); in the latter the energy is dispersed throughout the system as heat energy. In either of these events there is no permanent change, and the quantum efficiency is zero.

In some instances there may be the possibility of permanent change to an activated molecule, provided that in the brief period of excitation—before it must fluoresce or lose its energy by an unlucky encounter—it meets another molecule of a kind with which it can react. A proportion of activated molecules may thus undergo an irreversible change. This proportion may be affected by the temperature of the system and the concentrations of the various molecular species present.

For example, when a solution of anthracene is irradiated with ultra-violet light, some dianthracene is formed. The quantum efficiency depends on the concentration of anthracene but is not affected by the temperature. Writing A for an anthracene molecule, A_2 for dianthracene and A^* for an activated anthracene molecule, the primary process is,

$$A + h\nu \rightarrow A^*$$

while the secondary process can be either

$$A^* + A \rightarrow A_2$$

which yields a molecule of dianthracene, or,

$$A^* \rightarrow A + h\nu'$$

in which the activation energy is lost by fluorescence.

Which of these two alternative secondary processes occurs depends on the chance of the activated anthracene molecule meeting another anthracene molecule. The chance is less in a dilute solution than in a concentrated one. Consequently dilute solutions fluoresce strongly, and in these the quantum efficiency is low. In stronger solutions the fluorescence is less—and the yield of dianthracene more—up to the point (0·1 molar in anthracene) where the loss of energy by fluorescence is negligible. Further increase in concentration is then without effect on the quantum yield. Deactivation of excited molecules by collision with solvent molecules is not important in this reaction, as is shown by its indifference to temperature or the nature of the solvent.

Sometimes, following absorption of a quantum, an energy or atomic chain of reactions may be initiated. Thus in the photo-chemical reaction between hydrogen gas and chlorine gas, thousands of HCl molecules are formed for each quantum absorbed. The primary process is the absorption of a quantum by a chlorine molecule. In this instance the energy acquired is sufficient to raise the chlorine molecule to an unstable electronic level with the result that the molecule dissociates into atoms,

$$Cl_2 + h\nu \rightarrow Cl + Cl$$

If no other kinds of molecules are present these dissociated atoms will recombine to form the molecule again. If, however, hydrogen is present then the following reaction can occur,

$$Cl + H_2 \rightarrow HCl + H \qquad\qquad (a)$$

and the active hydrogen atom so formed can propagate a chain by reacting with an undissociated chlorine molecule as follows,

$$H + Cl_2 \rightarrow HCl + Cl \qquad \text{(b)}$$

The new Cl atom can then act as in equation (a) and the new H atom as in equation (b) and the chain continued until it is terminated by,

$$H + H \rightarrow H_2 \text{ or}$$
$$Cl + Cl \rightarrow Cl_2$$

Such atomic-chain (and energy-chain) reactions are sensitive to the concentrations of reactants and to the temperature.

Wherever there is the possibility of a chain reaction (causing high yields) or alternatively, where de-activation processes are predominant (causing low yields) the overall quantum efficiency is usually affected by the concentrations of reactants and by the temperature. Conversely, where these variables are without effect on the yield this is generally considered to be evidence that the reaction mechanism is a simple one, having an overall quantum efficiency in the region of unity.

THE METHOD OF PHOTOMETRIC CURVES

DARTNALL, GOODEVE and LYTHGOE (1936, 1938) made a quantitative analysis of the photochemical bleaching of visual purple solutions in monochromatic light using a new method subsequently termed (GOODEVE and WOOD, 1938) the method of photometric curves. This method consisted of an analysis of the transmission/time curves of bleaching solutions. The apparatus used is depicted in Fig. 3.2. The source was a 1000 c.p. tungsten arc, 'Pointolite,' lamp S, the light from which was focussed on to the entry slit, S_1, of a monochromator by means of the condensing lens and the totally reflecting prism R. After passing through the monochromator lens L, the light entered the front face of the prism P and then, after reflection from the silvered back face, was brought to a focus by L, as a spectrum in the plane of the slits. The dominant wavelength of that part of the spectrum which emerged from the exit slit S_2 could be altered by rotation of the prism, while the purity of the light delivered was governed by the widths of the exit and entry slits.

After emerging from the exit slit, the monochromatic beam passed through a small lens, V, which formed a circular image of the lens, L, on the aperture of the cell holder, H. This was made with passages to allow a flow of water through it from a thermostat, thus maintaining the temperature constant to within 1°C. The cylindrical optical cell (internal diameter 1·0 cm, length 0·5 cm) was of fused quartz with plane parallel faces. It fitted coaxially into a cavity in the holder, the aperture of which was of the same diameter as the

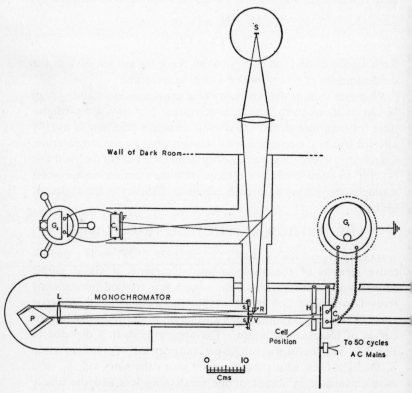

FIG. 3.2. Apparatus for studying the bleaching kinetics of photosensitive solutions by the method of photometric curves.
(*Dartnall, Goodeve and Lythgoe*, 1936)

cell. The beam of light from the exit slit was slightly divergent but the spreading over the short optical path through the visual purple solutions could be neglected.

After passing through the visual purple solution, the monochromatic beam fell on a photoelectric cell, C_1, which was connected to a critically-damped galvanometer, G_1. Between the cell holder and the photocell was a thin circular disc rotated by an electrical synchronous motor at exactly 1 r.p.m. A concentric slot of 180°C cut in this disc allowed the light transmitted by the visual purple to pass to the photocell for half a minute and screened it for the following half-minute. A galvanometer scale reading was taken 15 sec. after the shutter had opened and a 'zero' reading 15 sec. after it had closed. The difference between these readings was proportional to the output current of the photocell and hence proportional to the light trans-

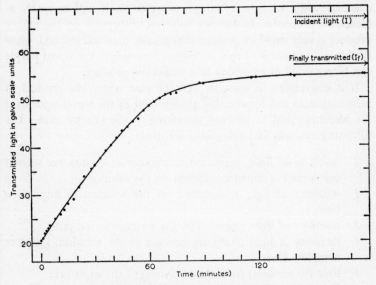

FIG. 3.3. Transmission/time curve of a visual purple solution when bleached by a constant-intensity light.

mitted by the visual purple solution. As the visual purple bleached, its transmission increased and there were corresponding increases in the galvanometer deflection.

The transmission/time curve for the first visual purple solution studied by this method is shown in Fig. 3.3. In this experiment the bleaching was carried out with blue-green light ($\lambda = 506$ mμ). The initial transmission of the solution, expressed in galvanometer scale units, was 20·5 and the final transmission, i.e. after the solution had been completely bleached by a prolonged exposure, was 57·0. The intensity of light actually incident on the solution (allowing for that reflected from the front surfaces of the cell) was 66·9 in the same units. Thus the initial optical density was 0·51 ($\log_{10} 66\cdot9/20\cdot5$) and that of the fully-bleached solution, 0·07.

ANALYSIS OF TRANSMISSION/TIME CURVES

When a solution of visual purple is 'bleached' its transmission may decrease or increase, depending on the wavelength of light used for measurement. Since the bleaching results in the formation of a yellow product, the transmissivity to violet light (for example) will decrease while to light of longer wavelength it will increase, as bleaching proceeds. In alkaline solution absorption by the yellow product is very small for wavelengths greater than 460 mμ and, when the bleaching light is of this, or longer, wavelength the visual purple can be regarded as bleaching to a colourless product.

It is convenient to consider first the case where the product of bleaching does not appreciably absorb light of the wavelength used for bleaching and to proceed therefrom to the general case. The following symbols and definitions are used:

I intensity of light, expressed as number of quanta per second per square centimetre, incident on the solution;

I_t intensity of light transmitted by the solution at any given time, t;

J_t intensity of light absorbed by the solution at the time, t;

I_f intensity of light finally transmitted by the solution, i.e. after complete bleaching;

t time (in seconds) from the beginning of the exposure;

l internal length (cm) of the optical cell;

A exposed area (cm^2) of the solution;

V volume (cm^3) of the solution;

n number of centres of absorption (chromophores) in the volume, V, of the solute;

c concentration of chromophores; thus $c = n/V$;

γ quantum efficiency, a ratio defined as

$$\frac{\text{number of chromophores destroyed}}{\text{number of quanta absorbed}};$$

α extinction coefficient per chromophore, expressed in cm^2 and defined by the equation

$$\log_e I/I_t = \alpha cl.$$

68

First case—non-absorbing impurities and photoproducts. In the first instance suppose that the visual purple solution is free from all light-absorbing impurities and that the bleaching is carried out by light which the photoproduct does not appreciably absorb.

Consider a parallel beam of the monochromatic light to fall on a solution contained in a cylindrical optical cell arranged coaxially with the direction of the light beam. It is assumed that Beer's and Lambert's laws of light absorption hold. These state that

$$J_t = I(1 - e^{-\alpha cl}).\tag{1}$$

Those layers of the visual purple solution which first receive the light beam weaken it for those at the rear. Consequently the front layers bleach before the rear ones. Nevertheless, equation (1) and the following argument hold when there is a concentration gradient along the optical axis, if it is understood that by c is meant the effective concentration at any time if the solution were mixed.

From the above definition of quantum efficiency, the rate of decrease in the number of chromophores is equal to the product of the quantum efficiency and the absorbed light intensity. That is

$$-\frac{dc}{dt} = \frac{\gamma J_t}{V}.\tag{2}$$

By eliminating J_t between (1) and (2),

$$-\frac{dc}{dt} = \frac{\gamma I}{V}\{1 - e^{-\alpha cl}\}$$

which, on rearranging, becomes

$$-\frac{dc}{(1 - e^{-\alpha cl})} = \frac{\gamma I}{V} . dt.\tag{3}$$

By making the assumption that γ, the quantum efficiency, is independent of concentration, (3) may be integrated to give

$$\log_e \frac{1}{e^{\alpha cl} - 1} = \frac{\alpha \gamma lI}{V} . t + \text{constant},$$

and, since $e^{\alpha cl} = I/I_t$ this becomes

$$\log_e \frac{I_t}{I - I_t} = \frac{\alpha \gamma I}{A} . t + \text{constant}.\tag{4}$$

69

In any experiment I and A are constants, and so are α and γ if the assumptions are justified. Thus by plotting $\log_e I_t/(I - I_t)$ against t, a straight line of slope $= \alpha\gamma I/A$ should be obtained. In general, however, this is not the case. While it is possible (by carrying out the bleaching with light of suitably long wavelength) to meet the requirement that the photoproduct does not absorb the bleaching light, it is less easy to ensure that the solutions are free from impurities which do. In the experiment just described (Fig. 3.3), for example, the solution had an optical density of 0·07 after complete bleaching. This solution, moreover, was one of the purest in DARTNALL, GOODEVE and LYTHGOE'S investigation, the final density in one instance being as high as 0·45—nearly all due to impurity. Consequently when $\log_e I_t/(I - I_t)$ was plotted against t, the results did not fall on a straight line but on a curve. In all cases, however, it was found that, if instead of $\log_e I_t/(I - I_t)$, $\log_e I_t/(I_f - I_t)$ were plotted against time, a straight line was obtained (see Fig. 3.4).

Second case—impurities absorbing, photoproducts non-absorbing. From the *experimental* result that

$$\log_e \frac{I_t}{I_f - I_t} = mt + \text{constant} \tag{5}$$

an expression for the bleaching of visual purple solutions which contain stable light-absorbing impurities can be deduced. As before it is assumed that the photoproducts do not absorb the bleaching light. In equation (5), the slope m of the line is not equal to $\alpha\gamma I/A$ but it can be shown (DARTNALL, 1936) to be related to this quantity by the equation,

$$m = \left\{ \frac{I_f}{I_f - I_t} \cdot \frac{I - I_t}{I} \cdot \frac{\log I_f/I_t}{\log I/I_t} \right\} \cdot \frac{\alpha\gamma I}{A}. \tag{6}$$

Substitution of this value of m in equation (5) gives the required equation,

$$\log_e \frac{I_t}{I_f - I_t} = \phi \frac{\alpha\gamma I}{A} . t + \text{constant} \tag{7}$$

where ϕ has been written for the quantity in brackets in equation (6).

At first sight it may seem that equations (5) and (7) are mutually exclusive—for m, the coefficient of t in equation (5), is constant (as shown by the fact that a straight line is obtained when the L.H.S. is

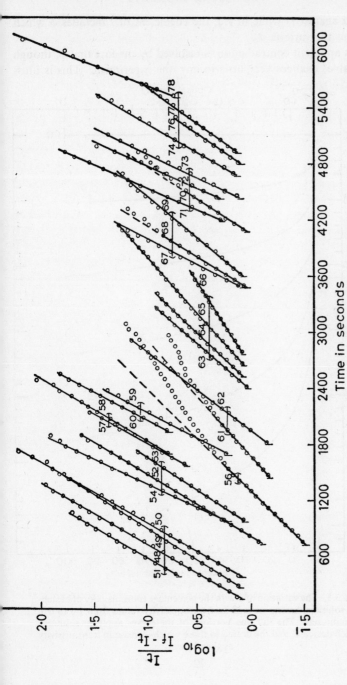

Fig. 3.4. The plot of $\log I_t/(I_f - I_t)$ against time for a number of different photometric curve experiments. Experiments 56, 61, and 68 (which were at 14·6, 10·7 and 10·0°C respectively) do not yield straight lines. Experiments 65 and 69 (5°C) and all the others (various temperatures between 20·2 and 60·0°C) yield straight lines.

(Dartnall, Goodeve and Lythgoe, 1938)

plotted against t) while in (7), the coefficient of t includes ϕ which contains the variable I_t.

This apparent contradiction is resolved by the fact that ϕ, though a variable, changes very little in any one experiment. This is illus-

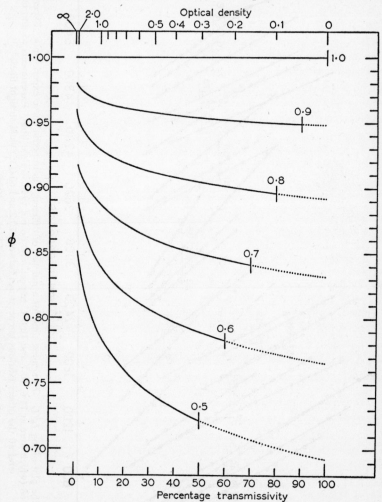

Fig. 3.5. The variation of ϕ with the percentage transmissivity of bleaching solutions having various final transmissivity values from 1·0 to 0·5, as indicated. The full line portions of the curves apply to solutions which decrease, and the dotted to those which increase in transmissivity as they bleach.

72

trated in Fig. 3.5 in which ϕ is plotted against the transmissivity for the range of values of I_f/I from 1·0 to 0·5. The case $I_f/I = 1·0$ corresponds to a final transmission of 100 per cent, i.e. to a solution quite free from absorbing impurities. In this instance the value of ϕ is invariant and equal to unity, and equation (7) reduces to the form of equation (4). The case $I_f/I = 0·5$ represents a final transmission of only 50 per cent, i.e. a density due to impurities of 0·3. Even in such an impure solution as this, however, the change in ϕ is quite small, provided the initial density of the solution (i.e. before bleaching) is not too high. The maximum variations in ϕ over the whole range of a bleaching curve, assuming an initial optical density of 0·5 (for example) and various values for the final transmissivity, I_f/I, are as follows:

I_f/I	1·0	0·9	0·8	0·5
Final density	0·0	0·046	0·097	0·301
Value of ϕ_0	1·0	0·957	0·910	0·740
Value of ϕ_∞	1·0	0·950	0·897	0·721
Variation	0	0·7%	1·4%	2·7%

General case. By means of the function ϕ, we may now solve the general case, viz. where not only are light-absorbing impurities present but where also the photo-product absorbs light of the wavelength used for bleaching.

Assuming that Beer's and Lambert's laws of light absorption hold for all components, the optical density of the solution at any time, t, is

$$\log_e \frac{I}{I_t} = \alpha c l + z\alpha'(c_0 - c)l + d_i, \tag{8}$$

where $z\alpha'$ has been written for $a\alpha_a + b\alpha_b + \ldots$; $\alpha_a, \alpha_b, \ldots$, being the extinction coefficients of the products of bleaching and $a, b, \ldots$, their stoichiometric relation to visual purple, d_i the density of the impurities present and c_0 the visual purple concentration when $t = 0$. Differentiating (8) with respect to time and rearranging the result,

$$-\frac{dI_t}{I_t \cdot dt} = (\alpha l - z\alpha' l)\frac{dc}{dt}. \tag{9}$$

6

From the definition of quantum efficiency, the rate of decrease in the number of visual purple chromophores, $-dn/dt$, is equal to the product of the quantum efficiency and the intensity of light absorbed by the visual purple. This latter quantity is related to the total light absorbed, $(I - I_t)$, by the ratio of αcl to the total density. We have, therefore,

$$-\frac{dn}{dt} \equiv -\frac{V dc}{dt} = \gamma \cdot \frac{\alpha cl}{\alpha cl + z\alpha'(c_0 - c)l + d_i} \cdot (I - I_t) \quad (10)$$

whence, by eliminating dc/dt between (9) and (10) and rearranging the result,

$$\frac{dI_t}{I_t dt} = \frac{\alpha cl - z\alpha' cl}{\alpha cl + z\alpha'(c_0 - c)l + d_i} \cdot \frac{I - I_t}{I} \cdot \frac{\alpha \gamma I}{A}. \quad (11)$$

Now the density of the completely bleached solution is

$$\log_e \frac{I}{I_f} = z\alpha' c_0 + d_i \quad (12)$$

and, subtracting equation (12) from equation (8),

$$\log_e \frac{I_f}{I_t} = \alpha cl - z\alpha' cl \quad (13)$$

whence, by substituting equations (8) and (13) in (11),

$$\frac{dI_t}{I_t dt} = \frac{\log_e I_f/I_t}{\log_e I/I_t} \cdot \frac{I - I_t}{I} \cdot \frac{\alpha \gamma I}{A}. \quad (14)$$

On multiplying both sides of this equation by $\dfrac{I_f}{I_f - I_t}$ we have,

$$\frac{I_f}{I_f - I_t} \cdot \frac{dI_t}{I_t dt} = \phi \frac{\alpha \gamma I}{A}. \quad (15)$$

Since, as we have seen, the function ϕ can be treated as a constant in any one experiment, equation (15) can be integrated to give,

$$\log_e \frac{I_t}{I_f - I_t} = \phi \frac{\alpha \gamma I}{A} \cdot t + \text{constant} \quad (16)$$

which is identical with the equation (7) obtained in the case where the products of bleaching were assumed to be non-absorbing. The same equation thus describes all possible conditions. The correcting function ϕ is a measure of the reduction in the rate of photodecomposition due to the presence of absorbing impurities and products of bleaching. At the end of an experiment, that is when all photochemical change has been completed, I_t is equal to I_f and ϕ is given by

$$\phi_\infty = \frac{I - I_f}{I} \cdot \frac{1}{\log_e I/I_f}.$$

Thus ϕ, since it is nearly independent of I_t, depends almost exclusively upon the values of I and I_f, that is on the final transmissivity.

At wavelengths shorter than about 420 mμ (in alkaline solution) the photoproducts absorb more strongly than the visual purple. When measured with short wavelength light therefore, the transmission of bleaching visual purple solutions decrease with time. In such cases I_f is always less than I_t and the appropriate ϕ functions are given by the dotted portions of the curves in Fig. 3.5. Also, the term $\log_e I_t/(I_f - I_t)$ in the L.H.S. of equation (16) must be replaced by $\log_e I_t/|I_f - I_t|$ where $|I_f - I_t|$, the modulus of $(I_f - I_t)$, is reckoned as a positive quantity irrespective of its real sign (GOODEVE, LYTHGOE and SCHNEIDER, 1942). The plot of $\log_e I_t/|I_f - I_t|$ against time then yields a straight line as in the cases where the transmission increases with time.

EXPERIMENTAL RESULTS

The equation

$$\log_{10} \frac{I_t}{I_f - I_t} = \phi \frac{\alpha\gamma I}{2 \cdot 3 A} \cdot t + \text{constant} \qquad (17)$$

(equation (16) restated in terms of decadic logarithms) is a general one, expressing the progress of any photo-chemical change. By plotting experimental values for the L.H.S. of the equation against time, a straight line is obtained having a slope equal to $\phi\alpha\gamma I/2 \cdot 3 A$. The quantity I/A, namely the quanta per second incident on each square centimetre of solution can be measured, and ϕ obtained from the transmissivities. Consequently $\alpha\gamma$, the product of the extinction coefficient and the quantum efficiency can be calculated. GOODEVE and WOOD (1938) proposed the term 'photosensitivity' for this product which is of greater practical importance than either the extinction coefficient or the quantum efficiency considered separately. Equation (17) occupies the same role in photochemistry as do the equations for first and second order thermal reactions, the photo-sensitivity corresponding to the reaction velocity constants. Equation (17) contains no concentration terms. Consequently the photo-sensitivity can be measured in solutions of unknown concentration. This makes the method of photometric curves of particular value in cases like that of visual purple.

The method of photometric curves is very sensitive to the presence of consecutive reactions and other complications and where these occur the plot of $\log_{10} I_t/(I_f - I_t)$ against t does not yield a straight line. The photochemical reaction in the bleaching of visual purple is the formation of transient orange. This substance then decomposes thermally to indicator yellow. At temperatures of 20°C and above this conversion is extremely fast. At the low light intensities used, the photochemical change to transient orange is the rate-determining reaction, all transient orange being removed (by thermal decomposition to indicator yellow) almost immediately after it is produced. This secondary process does not interfere, therefore, and the reaction proceeds as though visual purple were directly changed into indicator yellow. Straight lines were consequently obtained when $\log I_t/(I_f - I_t)$ was plotted against time, and the slope-compensating factor ϕ, depended only on the internal filter effect of indicator yellow. Below 20°C and above 5°C the conversion of transient orange to indicator yellow proceeded at a rate comparable with that of the photochemical change. Within this temperature range, therefore, the method of photometric curves broke down. At 5°C transient orange was fairly stable and its rate of conversion to indicator yellow was negligible in comparison with the photochemical reaction. Consequently when $\log I_t/(I_f - I_t)$ was plotted against time, straight lines were once again obtained. The reaction at this temperature was simply the conversion of visual purple into transient orange, and ϕ, the slope-compensating factor, depended on the internal filter effects of transient orange.

The maximum photosensitivity ($\alpha\gamma$). Using a bleaching light of wavelength 506 mμ (close to the λ_{max} for visual purple), DARTNALL, GOODEVE and LYTHGOE (1936, 1938) carried out a number of experiments under widely different conditions of pH (6·8–9·2) and temperature (5°–60°C). At the higher temperatures, allowances were made for the effect of thermal decomposition. In all cases, save for the range below 20°C and above 5°C, straight lines were obtained on plotting $\log I_t/(I_f - I_t)$ against time. This showed that the assumptions made in the theoretical treatment, viz. (1) that visual purple solutions obey Beer's and Lambert's laws, and (2) that the quantum efficiency does not depend on the concentration, were justified. Between 20°C and 60°C, $\alpha\gamma$, the photosensitivity was constant and had the value 9×10^{17} cm² per quantum absorbed. At 5°C the value was slightly less (7×10^{-17}). Subsequently, BRODA and GOODEVE (1941) showed that even at $- 73$°C a glycerol-water solution of visual purple had a photodecomposition rate of the same order as at room temperature.

The photosensitivity is a measure of the rate of a photochemical reaction. The value for visual purple is among the highest recorded for any substance. It is comparable, for example, with that for the hydrogen-chlorine reaction which, though having a quantum efficiency (γ) of between 10^3 and 10^5, yet has an extinction coefficient (α) of only about 10^{-21} cm².

The quantum efficiency (γ). Since the absorption characteristics (α) of visual purple do not change markedly with pH nor with temperature, the constancy of $\alpha\gamma$ over wide ranges of these variables indicates a constant value for γ, the quantum efficiency. The lower values obtained at 5°C suggest that some deactivation may have set in at this temperature.

The constancy of $\alpha\gamma$ also provides a strong argument against the secondary process being a chain reaction, for such reactions are almost invariably influenced by temperature, and commonly by concentration. One may therefore conclude that γ is not greater than unity. It is less easy to estimate the relative probability of deactivation (and hence of a low value for γ) except to say that a high deactivation fraction could not easily be reconciled with the observed constancy of the photochemical bleaching rate irrespective of variations in temperature, pH, and solvent. Thus γ is either equal to, or not much less than, unity (DARTNALL, GOODEVE and LYTHGOE, 1936, 1938).

The variation of photosensitivity with wavelength. The spectral variation of the photosensitivity of frog visual purple was measured by GOODEVE, LYTHGOE and SCHNEIDER (1939, 1942). The results obtained are shown in Fig. 3.6 (filled circles). TRENDELENBURG'S (1904) bleaching values—as corrected by HENRI and LARGUIER DES BANCELS (1911) for the energy distribution of the Nernst lamp spectrum, and brought to an equal quantum intensity basis—are shown by the unfilled circles. They are in reasonably good agreement with the modern values.

When GOODEVE, LYTHGOE and SCHNEIDER's measurements were made the density spectrum of visual purple was known accurately only at wavelengths longer than about 430 mμ. The density spectrum of a visual purple solution determined at this time by GOODEVE,

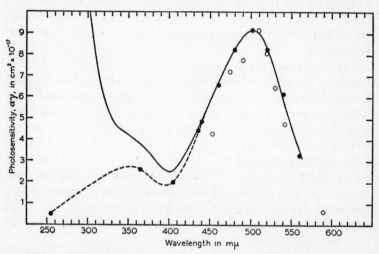

FIG. 3.6. Comparison of the photosensitivity and density spectra of visual purple. ●, Goodeve, Lythgoe and Schneider's values for the photo-sensitivity; ○, Trendelenburg's 'bleaching values,' after correction as described in text. Full line curve, density spectrum of a visual purple solution equated at 500 mμ to the photosensitivity.

(*After Schneider, Goodeve and Lythgoe, 1939 and Goodeve, Lythgoe and Schneider, 1942*)

LYTHGOE and WOOD is shown by the full line in Fig. 3.6. It will be seen that there is an accurate coincidence between the photo-sensitivity ($\alpha\gamma$) and the density (α) at all wavelengths above 430 mμ indicating that γ, the quantum efficiency, is independent of wavelength over at least this range.

Although, because of yellow impurities, the density spectrum does not coincide with the $\alpha\gamma$ data below 430 mμ, a maximum at 350–360 mμ and a minimum at 400 mμ is common to both sets of measurements. From this GOODEVE, LYTHGOE and SCHNEIDER concluded that the band at 350–360 mμ is closely connected with the visual purple chromophore, and corresponds to a transition to a higher electronic level than that for the characteristic band at 500 mμ.

REDUCTION OF OVERALL QUANTUM YIELD
BY REGENERATION

In the preceding arguments for a quantum efficiency of unity, 'or not much less,' no consideration was given to the possibility that the bleaching of visual purple might be a partially reversible process. If a solution of visual purple is bleached by exposing it to a bright light for several minutes and is then placed in darkness, there is normally little or no regeneration. But in these circumstances, any regeneration must be from indicator yellow, for by the beginning of the darkness period little or no transient orange is left in the solution.

In the 'photometric curves' experiments, however, the course of bleaching was followed continuously by measuring the change in transmittancy of the solution as it bleached. Only feeble bleaching lights from a monochromator were used and, within the temperature range 20–60°C, the thermal conversion of the photoproduct, transient orange, to indicator yellow was a much more rapid process than its production from visual purple. Consequently the reaction proceeded as though it were a straight forward bleaching of visual purple direct to indicator yellow. Nevertheless, transient orange had an ephemeral existence in the solutions. Any visual purple regenerated from transient orange would have had to be bleached again, leading to a low value for the photosensitivity.

Is there appreciable regeneration of visual purple from transient orange? Our knowledge of this phenomenon is due to some important observations by COLLINS and MORTON (1950b). Their procedure was as follows. After measuring the density spectrum of a visual purple solution they transferred it to a 30 ml beaker. The 2–3 ml of solution formed a thin layer which was frozen by lowering the beaker into alcohol at − 70°C. The frozen solution was then exposed to a bright light for 30 min. Under these circumstances (− 70°C) the bleaching of visual purple was arrested at the transient orange stage. The frozen bleached solution was thawed in darkness and kept at room temperature for 1 hr. During this period regeneration of photosensitive pigment from transient orange occurred. The density spectrum of the regenerated solution was then measured. The whole procedure—freezing of solution at − 70°C in darkness, irradiation, thawing in darkness, and measurement of density spectrum—was repeated a number of times.

The results of an experiment with frogs' visual purple are given in Fig. 3.7. The 'regenerated' pigment (iso-rhodopsin) differs slightly from the original one. This is shown by the different density maximum (at 493 mμ in place of 502 mμ) and by the fact that the curves for the first, second, third and fourth regeneration stages, and for the final bleached solution all pass through an isosbestic point—at about

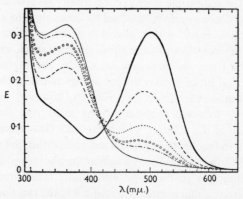

FIG. 3.7. Formation of an isomer of visual purple. Heavy continuous curve is the density spectrum of a frog's visual purple solution. This was completely bleached at −70°C and then allowed to reach room-temperature equilibrium in darkness (−−−−). Succeeding curves show the results obtained when this procedure was repeated three times. The final continuous curve was obtained after complete bleaching at room temperature. Note that the λ_{max} for the 'regenerated' pigment (iso-rhodopsin) differs from the original visual purple.

(*Collins and Morton*, 1950b)

415 mμ—which does not lie on the curve for the original pigment. Similar results were obtained with the visual purple (λ_{max} = 497–500 mμ) of rats and of oxen, except that the regenerated iso-rhodopsin had λ_{max} at 487–488 mμ.

As Fig. 3.7 shows, the amount of pigment regenerated in each darkness period was about 50 per cent of that originally present. This was confirmed by WALD, DURELL and ST. GEORGE (1950) who showed, in addition, that similar results were obtained at room temperature when visual purple in a dry gelatine film was bleached, and then moistened in darkness (see Figs. 2.9 and 2.10).

To explain the 50 per cent regeneration, COLLINS and MORTON

supposed that the transient orange chromophores underwent a dismutation reaction; half of them losing an electron to give indicator yellow and the other half gaining an electron to yield iso-rhodopsin.

COLLINS and MORTON assumed that the dismutation of transient orange to iso-rhodopsin and indicator yellow must also have taken

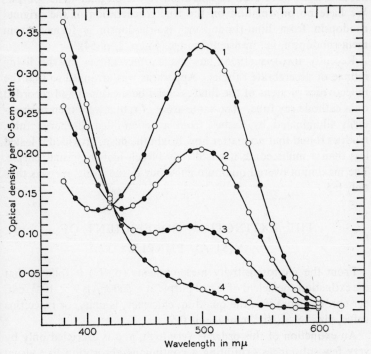

FIG. 3.8. The partial bleaching of a frog's visual purple solution at 20°C. Curve 1 density spectrum of unbleached solution; curve 2, after 1 hr bleaching with light of dominant wavelength 580 mμ; curve 3, after a further 2 hr, curve 4, after a further 17 hr. Note the isosbestic point and absence of evidence for iso-rhodopsin (cf. Fig. 3.7).

place in the experiments of DARTNALL, GOODEVE and LYTHGOE, with consequent reduction of the overall quantum yield to one half. But when a visual purple solution is bleached under similar conditions to those in the experiments of DARTNALL *et al.*, no iso-rhodopsin is formed (DARTNALL, unpublished). For example, in Fig. 3.8, curve 1 is the original density spectrum of a visual purple solution and curves 2, 3 and 4, respectively, the density spectra after 1 hr, 3 hr and 20 hr exposure to yellow light of dominant wavelength 570 mμ. All the curves pass through an isosbestic point and the difference spectra formed by subtracting one curve from another are the same. This shows that iso-rhodopsin is not formed under these conditions (pH 7·7, temperature = 20°C). If any regeneration did occur it must have been regeneration to the original visual purple. We have no information on the true regeneration of the original rhodopsin from lumi-rhodopsin; iso-rhodopsin is formed from meta-rhodopsin, i.e. transient orange (Chap. 2, p. 54).

Recently HAGINS (1955) has made observations on the living retinae of decerebrate rabbits. Apparatus was arranged so that the reflectivities of areas of the fundus could be measured and recorded on a cathode ray tube. The same areas of retina were then momentarily illuminated by flashes from a xenon-filled discharge tube. HAGINS found that no matter how bright the flash, provided it lasted less than a millisecond, it could only bleach half the visual purple. The maximum overall quantum efficiency in the living eye was thus only 0·5.

THE EXTINCTION COEFFICIENT OF VISUAL PURPLE

From the photosensitivity measurements (p. 77) it follows that the extinction coefficient of visual purple at c. 500 mμ is 9×10^{-17} cm^2 per chromophore if γ, the quantum efficiency, is unity, or twice this value, viz. $1\cdot8 \times 10^{-16}$ cm^2 if γ is 0·5.

An extinction of this order is very high, and is exceeded only by very few substances exhibiting a continuous absorption like visual purple.

There is a theoretical limit to the magnitude of an extinction coefficient (BRAUDE, 1945). The extinction coefficient, α, is defined by the relation

$$\log_e \frac{I}{I_t} = \alpha c l.$$

On the R.H.S. of the equation the concentration, c (in number of chromophores per cubic centimetre) has dimensions $[L]^{-3}$, and l the optical path length has dimensions $[L]$. Consequently α must have the dimensions $[L]^2$ in order that the R.H.S., like the L.H.S. (which is a ratio) shall be dimensionless. An extinction coefficient is, therefore, an area and may be regarded as the product of the physical area of the chromophore and a probability factor expressing the chance that a quantum within this area is absorbed. The maximum value of the probability term is unity, and consequently the maximum possible extinction is given by the chromophore area. This is likely to be of the order 10^{-16}–10^{-15} cm^2. Thus the extinction of visual purple is of the same order as the theoretical maximum.

The molar extinction coefficient, ε, is given by the relation

$$\log_{10} \frac{I}{I_t} = \varepsilon c l$$

where the concentration, c, is in number of gram-molecules per litre. Conversion to these units is effected by multiplying α by $6 \cdot 1 \times 10^{23}$ (Avogadro's number), by $0 \cdot 43$ (natural to common logarithms) and by c. 10^{-3} (cubic centimetres to litres). If the maximum photosensitivity is expressed in these units we have $\varepsilon \gamma = 24{,}000n$, i.e. if $\gamma = 0 \cdot 5$, $\varepsilon = 48{,}000n$, where n is the number of chromophores in each visual purple molecule.

An independent estimate of the molar extinction coefficient was obtained by COLLINS and MORTON (1950a) from the relations between the density spectra of visual purple and of its derivatives indicator yellow and retinene. The molar extinctions of the latter substances could be directly measured. COLLINS and MORTON found that $\varepsilon_{\max}$ for visual purple $= 48{,}000p \cdot n$, where p is the number (now known to be one) of C_{20} (i.e. retinene or vitamin A) units in the visual purple chromophore, and n, as before, the number of chromophores per molecule. WALD and BROWN (1953) obtained the value $40{,}600n$ in a similar investigation in which possible complications, arising from the cis-trans isomerization of visual purple derivatives, were eliminated.

HAGINS (1954) measured the photosensitivity of visual purple *in situ* in the excised eyes of rabbits. He obtained the value 27,000, indicating (if $\gamma = 0 \cdot 5$) that $\varepsilon_{\max} = 54{,}000n$. This high result was expected since the visual purple molecules as oriented in the retinal rods have an extinction about 50 per cent higher than in solution. HAGINS found that digitonin solutions of rabbit visual purple, solidified as agar gells but otherwise treated in the same way, had a much lower photosensitivity (17,000).

The various estimates for the photosensitivity and extinction of visual purple are assembled in the following table.

Reference	Photo-sensitivity ($\varepsilon_{max}\,\gamma$)	Molar extinction (ε_{max})
Dartnall, Goodeve and Lythgoe (1936, 1938) (Solutions of frog visual purple)	23.000 (at 506 mμ)	(46,000n)
Schneider, Goodeve and Lythgoe (1939) (Solutions of frog visual purple)	24,000	(48,000n)
Collins and Morton (1950a) (Solutions of frog visual purple)	—	48,000p . n
Wald and Brown (1953) (Solutions of cattle visual purple)	—	40,600p . n
Hagins (1954) (Excised rabbit eyes) (Rabbit visual purple in agar gels)	27,000 17,000	(54,000n) (34,000n)

The bracketed values for ε_{max} have been calculated from photosensitivity measurements, assuming $\gamma = 0.5$; p is the number of C_{20} (retinene or vitamin A) units per chromophore; n is the number of chromophores in a visual purple molecule.

2. THERMOCHEMISTRY

Although solutions of visual purple, when kept in darkness, are very stable at room temperature, some decomposition can be detected over long periods. The product of thermal bleaching appears to be the same as when solutions are bleached by light and shows the same reversible colour changes with pH as does indicator yellow. The rate of thermal decomposition increases sharply with rising temperature; for example at 70°C the colour of solutions is destroyed in a few seconds.

LYTHGOE and QUILLIAM (1938) studied the thermal decomposition of visual purple throughout a wide range of conditions. The optical densities of solutions maintained at constant temperatures were measured at regular time intervals at two different wavelengths,

84

namely at 502 mμ (the λ_{max} for visual purple) and at the isosbestic wavelength appropriate to the pH of the solution. An isosbestic wavelength (see Fig. 2.11) is a wavelength for which the density of visual purple is the same as that of its product of bleaching (indicator yellow). Any density loss at such a wavelength showed that the indicator yellow was itself thermally decomposing. When this was the case, suitable corrections (calculated from the magnitude of the observed loss and the known absorption spectrum of indicator yellow at the particular pH) were made to the changes observed at 502 mμ.

The changes measured at 502 (after correction where necessary) were thus due to the decomposition of visual purple only. Density losses due to photochemical bleaching by the light used in measurement were negligibly small.

LYTHGOE and QUILLIAM found that under all conditions of pH (from 4·2 to 10·7) and temperature (from 31° to 56°C) the time course of thermal decomposition could be described by the equation

$$\log_e \frac{D_0 - D_f}{D_t - D_f} = kt$$

where D_t was the density of the solution at time t (sec), D_0 the initial density, and D_f the final density when all the visual purple had been bleached; $D_0 - D_f$ was thus a measure of the initial concentration of visual purple and $D_t - D_f$ a corresponding measure at time t. The value of the constant k depended on the pH and temperature.

In Fig. 3.9 the logarithms of the velocity constants k so found are plotted against the reciprocal of the absolute temperature. It is evident that for any given pH the data fall on a straight line and, consequently, that the Arrhenius equation is obeyed. This states that

$$\log_e k = C - E/RT$$

where C is a constant, R is the gas constant, T is the absolute temperature and E is the heat of activation of the reaction. The heat of activation can be calculated from the slopes of the straight lines in Fig. 3.9. For all lines except that for pH 4·2 the slopes are roughly the same and correspond to an activation energy of approximately 44,000 calories per gram-molecule. The results in Fig. 3.9 show that visual purple is most stable in neutral solution. A high salt content (see lower dotted line in Fig. 3.9) also reduces the rate of thermal decomposition.

THE CONTRIBUTION OF INTERNAL ENERGY TO THE PHOTO-CHEMICAL BLEACHING OF VISUAL PURPLE

The fact that the visual purple molecule can be 'bleached' either photochemically (by absorption of a quantum) or thermally (by a chance-accession of the energy of activation) led ST. GEORGE (1952) 'to study the transition between photic and thermal activation.' He considered that 'on going from shorter wavelengths to red light a point should be reached beyond which the incident quanta cannot

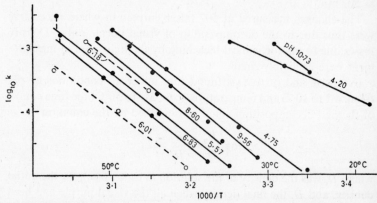

FIG. 3.9. The influence of temperature on the rate of thermal decomposition of frog's visual purple at various acidities. Abscissae: $1{,}000/T$, where T is the absolute temperature. Ordinates: $\log_{10}K$, where K is the velocity constant (time in seconds, natural logarithms). The upper dotted line is for a dialysed solution of low salt content; the lower dotted line for one containing added salt (2M NaCl).

(*Lythgoe and Quilliam*, 1938)

supply the entire energy needed to activate the rhodopsin molecule. There should therefore be a critical wavelength beyond which the bleaching by light becomes temperature-dependent.'

To investigate this possibility, ST. GEORGE measured the rates of photochemical bleaching (in digitonin solutions buffered at pH 6–7) at 2°C and at 32°C. The bleaching lights, of various wavelengths between 400 and 750 mμ, were obtained by passing the output from a high-power projection lamp through suitable interference filters.

The visual purple solutions (prepared both from cattle and from frog retinae) were contained in thermostatted quartz cells of dimensions 3 × 10 mm. The bleaching light traversed the short dimension and was then reflected back through the solution. This augmented the bleaching effect and also tended to eliminate the concentration gradient in the visual purple solution arising from a one-way transmission. The progress of the bleaching was followed by periodic measurements of the transmission at right angles, i.e. along the

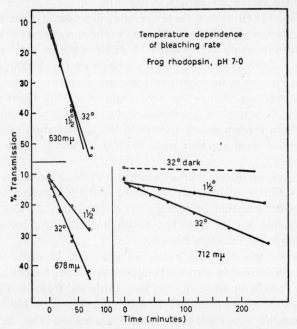

FIG. 3.10. Transmission/time curves at $1\frac{1}{2}°$ and 32°C for visual purple solutions bleaching under constant intensity lights of various wavelengths, as indicated. Transmissions were measured with light of 500 mμ wavelength. The broken line shows the change in transmission in darkness at 32°C.

(*St. George*, 1952)

10 mm dimension. In the bleaching experiments at 2°C the solution was warmed up to 30°C on each occasion before a transmission reading was taken, to allow intermediates (transient orange) to be converted to the final product.

Examples of the transmission/time curves obtained are given in Fig. 3.10. These show that the reaction is independent of temperature with a bleaching light of wavelength 530 mμ but is much affected by temperature with bleaching lights of 678 mμ or 712 mμ. In general it was found that when the bleaching light was of any wavelength between 400 and 590 mμ the bleaching rates were the same at 32°C as at 2°C, but that when it was of longer wavelength, i.e. between 590 and 750 mμ, there was a marked dependence on temperature. The ratios of the bleaching rates at 32°C and 2°C (Q_{30}) are plotted against wavelength in Fig. 3.11.

As Fig. 3.11 (B) shows, the temperature dependence of the bleaching rate begins at c. 590 mμ. The size of the energy unit (quantum) for this wavelength corresponds to 48,500 calories per 'mole of quanta.' This is quite close to the activation energy, 44,000 calories per gram-molecule, found by LYTHGOE and QUILLIAM for the purely thermal reaction. Up to the wavelength of 590 mμ therefore the energy of the quantum is adequate but at longer wavelengths—for which the quantum energy falls short of the activation energy—a contribution must be taken from the thermal energy stores of the molecule.

The question therefore arises whether only those molecules which have a sufficient internal energy to make up the deficit can absorb an 'inadequate' quantum, or whether any molecule can—in which case some quanta will be absorbed to no purpose, with consequent reduction in the quantum efficiency.

To settle this question, allowance must first be made for the changes in extinction with temperature. ST. GEORGE measured the density spectra, up to 620 mμ, of both cattle and frog visual purple solutions at various temperatures between 23°C and − 100°C. No measurements were made at 32°C but it was assumed that the ratios of the extinctions at 32°C to those at 2°C would be given sufficiently closely by the ratios at 25°C to those at − 5°C. The logarithms of these ratios, when plotted as a function of wavelength gave a straight line between 560 and 620 mμ. ST. GEORGE therefore extrapolated this line to 750 mμ to obtain estimates of the extinction ratios at those wavelengths where the density of the visual purple was too small to be directly measured.

In Fig. 3.11 (A) the extinction ratios so obtained are compared with the observed bleaching rate ratios. Although the general trend of variation with wavelength is the same for both, ST. GEORGE considered that the bleaching rate ratios were significantly higher than the extinction ratios. In this case 'the internal energy of the rhodopsin molecule is a more critical factor in bleaching than it is in the process of light absorption. Some of the molecules which absorbed

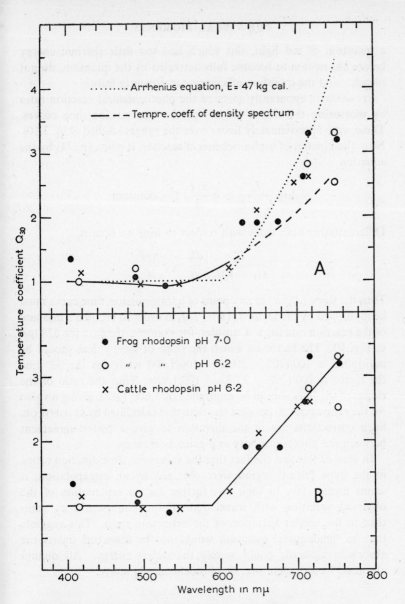

Fig. 3.11. The variation of the temperature coefficient (Q_{30}) of the bleaching rate with wavelength. (A) Results are compared with the temperature coefficient of the extinction of visual purple (lower curve) and also with a function calculated from the Arrhenius equation, assuming that a total activation energy of 47,000 calories per gm mol is required. (B) The two straight lines drawn through the results show that the bleaching rate becomes temperature-dependent at about 590 mμ.

(*St. George*, 1952)

a quantum of red light, but which had too little thermal energy before absorption to become fully activated by the quantum, do not bleach; and the quantum efficiency consequently falls.'

ST. GEORGE apparently assessed the photochemical reaction rates by measuring the slopes (dI_t/dt) of the transmission/time curves. These were approximately linear over the ranges studied (Fig. 3.10). Now the kinetics of a photochemical reaction is given (p. 74) by the equation

$$\log \frac{I_t}{I_f - I_t} = \phi \, \frac{\alpha\gamma I}{A} \cdot t + \text{constant}$$

Differentiating both sides with respect to time we obtain,

$$\frac{I_f}{(I_f - I_t)I_t} \cdot \frac{dI_t}{dt} = \phi \, \frac{\alpha\gamma I}{A}$$

Thus the slope (dI_t/dt) at any point of a transmission/time curve must be multiplied by the factor $I_f/(I_f - I_t)I_t$ in order to become a measure of the reaction rate $(\alpha\gamma)$. Consider, for example, the data for 678 mμ in Fig. 10. The factor by which the slope of the $1\frac{1}{2}°$ line should be multiplied is $100/(100 - 20)20 = 100/1,600$ while for the 32° line the factor is $100/(100 - 27)27 = 100/1,970$. Thus the ratio of the slopes of the lines should be multiplied by $1,600/1,970$, giving a value for the ratio about 20 per cent less than that calculated by ST. GEORGE. Such corrections are in the direction to give a better agreement between the photosensitivity and extinction ratios.

In view of this and the fact that the values for the extinction ratios in the most critical region were obtained by an extrapolation, it seems unnecessary to look any further for an explanation of the observed variation with wavelength of the photosensitivity ratio than to the similar variation of the extinction ratio. This suggests that an 'inadequate' quantum would not be absorbed unless the absorbing molecule could supply the deficit energy. All quanta absorbed would, therefore, be photochemically active.

3. MOLECULAR WEIGHT

THE WEIGHT OF THE CHROMOPHORE CARRIER

Visual purple is a chromoprotein. Like haemoglobin, ovoverdin, and other members of this class of coloured proteins, its molecule consists of one or more chromophores in association with a molecule of protein.

If M is the molecular weight of a chromoprotein, and n is the number of chromophores in each molecule of protein then R, the 'molecular' weight of that fraction of the chromoprotein molecule which contains one chromophore, is given by,

$$R = \frac{M}{n}$$

The fraction R may be called the carrier weight, for it is approximately equal to the weight of protein required to 'carry' one chromophore. Strictly speaking, the carrier weight should be defined through the molecular weight of the protein itself (i.e. without chromophores), but the difference is very small in practice since the chromophore is always very much lighter than the protein.

The value of R for visual purple was determined by BRODA, GOODEVE and LYTHGOE (1940) in the following way. The optical density, D, of a solution is given by,

$$D = \log_{10} \frac{I}{I_t} = \varepsilon c l$$

where ε is the molar extinction coefficient, c is the concentration in gram-molecules per litre and l is the optical path length in centimetres. From the photosensitivity measurements the value of ε per chromophore was known (assuming $\gamma = 1$) and therefore the molecular concentration of a visual purple solution could be calculated from its optical density. Consequently, by measuring the actual concentration of a solution, in grams per cubic centimetre, the carrier weight could be calculated.

BRODA, GOODEVE and LYTHGOE prepared visual purple solutions from the frog, and, after measuring the optical densities at 500 mμ in a 1 cm cell, estimated the dry weights of the visual purple in known volumes. Impurities (digitonin, salts and phospholipins) were either eliminated from the solutions by exhaustive dialysis and electrodialysis, or subsequently separated from the gross evaporation residues by the use of selective solvents.

The best experiment yielded the value 34,500 for the carrier weight, R. However, the solid residue had a nitrogen content of only 12 per cent. Since pure proteins contain 15–19 per cent N, the residue can have contained, at the most, only 80 per cent of pure visual purple protein. Assuming the impurities (20 per cent or more) to be phospholipins, with a nitrogen content of 1·8 per cent, BRODA, GOODEVE and LYTHGOE therefore arrived at the value 26,500 for an upper limit to R.

In these calculations, the molar extinction coefficient of the chromophore was taken to be 23,000, a value derived from the photo-sensitivity results on the assumption that $\gamma = 1$. As we have seen, however (p. 79 *et seq*.), there are grounds for believing that γ was 0·5 or thereabouts in the photometric curve experiments.

If WALD and BROWN'S value 40,600p for the extinction per chromo-phore is used, the carrier weight (upper limit) recalculated from BRODA, GOODEVE and LYTHGOE'S data, is 45,000p. Thus the molecular weight of visual purple (upper limit) as indicated by this method, is 45,000$p . n$, where p is the number of C_{20} units (retinene or vitamin A) in a chromophore and n is the number of chromo-phores in a molecule.

MOLECULAR WEIGHT

A theoretical estimate. In 1949, WEALE suggested that the molecu-lar weight of a dissolved substance could be estimated from the shape and position of its main absorption band and its optical density in a solution of known concentration. Starting from an equation developed by HOUSTOUN (1909), WEALE (1949a) showed that the molecular weight, M, was given by

$$M = K . p . \frac{w}{v} . \frac{1}{D . r} . \frac{\lambda^2_{max}}{\lambda_{\frac{1}{2} max} - \lambda_{max}}$$

where K was a known universal constant, p, the number of electrons (per molecule) responsible for the band, w/v, the concentration and D and r the optical density and refractive index, respectively, at the maximum.

For visual purple, λ_{max} and $\lambda_{\frac{1}{2} max}$ are, respectively, 5,020 and 5,480$A°$. Assuming $p = 1$, $r = 1·33$ and using BRODA, GOODEVE and LYTHGOE'S w/v and D data for their best solution, WEALE calculated the molecular weight of visual purple to be 45,600.

WEALE'S method was criticized by COLLINS and MORTON (1949) and more recently by HUBBARD (1954) mainly because of the arbitrary choice of unity for p, the number of electrons responsible for the band. It is not possible, at present, to assess the value of the method but, as WEALE (1949b) pointed out, 'the empirical device of putting $p \approx 1$ . . . makes it possible to predict the right order of the molecular weights of several substances.'

Measurements in the ultracentrifuge. The size and weight of colloidal particles can sometimes be inferred from their behaviour in the Svedburg ultracentrifuge. In this apparatus solutions can be subjected to a force exceeding a million times that of gravity. Under these conditions, colloidal particles and large molecular aggregates— if they are heavy enough—slowly sediment out of solution. By observing the movement of the upper boundary of the particles, one can determine whether the system is monodisperse, i.e. contains particles of uniform size, or is polydisperse. In the latter case the boundary is diffuse or, sometimes, multiple.

HECHT and PICKELS (1938) found that digitonin solutions of frog visual purple sedimented as particles of uniform size with a molecular weight of 270,000. For some time this was believed to be the molecular weight of visual purple. In 1940, however, SMITH and PICKELS reported that solutions of digitonin alone behaved in the ultracentrifuge as a monodisperse system having a micellar weight of at least 75,000. Each digitonin micelle therefore contained about 60 molecules of digitonin (M.W. = 1,288).

In a recent investigation, HUBBARD (1954) repeated and extended the earlier measurements. She found that visual purple solutions (from cattle retinae) sedimented as a stoichiometric complex ('RD-1') of visual purple and digitonin. The composition of this complex was not affected by the hydrogen ion concentration (between pH 6·3 and 9·6) nor by the presence of excess digitonin. From the sedimentation constant, HUBBARD calculated that the molecular weight of RD-1 was 260,000–290,000, thus confirming the earlier observations of HECHT and PICKELS.

The relative proportions of digitonin and visual purple in the RD-1 complex were obtained by analysis of solutions which contained only RD-1. The digitonin was estimated by its haemolytic activity; the visual purple, by measuring the nitrogen content of the solutions and assuming that visual purple contains 15 per cent N. It was found that 14 per cent of the weight of the complex, i.e. 36,000–41,000, was due to visual purple.

HUBBARD deduced the molecular weight of visual purple in the following way. From her own data it could be calculated that a visual purple solution which had an optical density at 500 mμ of 1·0 per cm, would contain 2·4–2·7 $\times$ 10^{-8} moles of RD-1 per litre.

Again, from WALD and BROWN's value for the molecular extinction coefficient of visual purple, viz. 40,600 cm² per mole equivalent of retinene (p. 83) it follows that such a solution would contain $2 \cdot 5 \times 10^{-8}$ moles of retinene. In other words, the molar concentration of RD-1 and retinene are equal. From this HUBBARD concluded 'RD-1 contains one molecule of rhodopsin, with a molecular weight of about 40,000, and carrying a single chromophore composed of one molecule of retinene.'

REFERENCES

BRAUDE, E. A. (1945). Intensities of light absorption. *Nature, Lond.*, **155**, 753–754.

BRODA, E. E., GOODEVE, C. F. and LYTHGOE, R. J. (1940). The weight of the chromophore carrier in the visual purple molecule. *J. Physiol.*, **98**, 397–404.

BRODA, E. E. and GOODEVE, C. F. (1941). The behaviour of visual purple at low temperature. *Proc. roy. Soc. A.*, **179**, 151–159.

COLLINS, F. D. and MORTON, R. A. (1949). Absorption spectra, molecular weights and visual purple. *Nature, Lond.*, **164**, 528–529.

COLLINS, F. D. and MORTON, R. A. (1950a). Studies on rhodopsin. 2. Indicator yellow. *Biochem. J.*, **47**, 10–17.

COLLINS, F. D. and MORTON, R. A. (1950b). Studies in rhodopsin. 3. Rhodopsin and transient orange. *Biochem. J.*, **47**, 18–24.

DARTNALL, H. J. A. (1936). The photochemistry of visual processes. Ph.D. Thesis., Univ. of London.

DARTNALL, H. J. A., GOODEVE, C. F. and LYTHGOE, R. J. (1936). The quantitative analysis of the photochemical bleaching of visual purple solutions in monochromatic light. *Proc. roy. Soc. A.*, **156**, 158–170.

DARTNALL, H. J. A., GOODEVE, C. F. and LYTHGOE, R. J. (1938). The effect of temperature on the photochemical bleaching of visual purple solutions. *Proc. roy. Soc. A.*, **164**, 216–230.

GOODEVE, C. F., LYTHGOE, R. J. and SCHNEIDER, E. E. (1942). The photosensitivity of visual purple solutions and the scotopic sensitivity of the eye in the ultra-violet. *Proc. roy. Soc. B.*, **130**, 380–395.

GOODEVE, C. F. and WOOD, L. J. (1938). The photosensitivity of diphenylamine *p*-diazonium sulphate by the method of photometric curves. *Proc. roy. Soc. A.*, **166**, 342–353.

HAGINS, W. A. (1954). The photosensitivity of mammalian rhodopsin *in situ*. *J. Physiol.*, **126**, 37P.

HAGINS, W. A. (1955). The quantum efficiency of bleaching of rhodopsin *in situ*. *J. Physiol.*, **129**, 22P.

HECHT, S. (1920). Photochemistry of visual purple. I: The kinetics of the decomposition of visual purple by light. *J. gen. Physiol.*, **3**, 1–13.

HECHT, S. (1921). Photochemistry of visual purple. II: The effect of temperature on the bleaching of visual purple by light. *J. gen. Physiol.*, **3**, 285–290.

HECHT, S. (1924). Photochemistry of visual purple. III: The relation between intensity of light and the rate of bleaching of visual purple. *J. gen. Physiol.*, **6**, 731–740.

HECHT, S. and PICKELS, E. G. (1938). The sedimentation constant of visual purple. *Proc. nat. Acad. Sci. Wash.*, **24**, 172–176.

HENRI, V. and LARGUIER DES BANCELS, J. (1911). Photochimie de la rétine. *J. Phys. Path. gén.*, **13**, 841–856.

HOUSTOUN, R. A. (1909). On the mechanism of the absorption spectra of solutions. *Proc. roy. Soc. A.*, **82**, 606–611.

HUBBARD, R. (1954). The molecular weight of rhodopsin and the nature of the rhodopsin-digitonin complex. *J. gen. Physiol.*, **37**, 381–399.

KÖGEL, G. (1929). Neue Forschungsergebnisse der Photochemie des Sehpurpurs. *Phot. Korr.*, **65**, 248–249.

KÖNIG, A. (1894). Über den menschlichen Sehpurpur und seine Bedeutung für das Sehen. *S.B. Preuss. Akad. Wiss.*, **30**, 577–598.

LYTHGOE, R. J. and QUILLIAM, J. P. (1938). The thermal decomposition of visual purple. *J. Physiol.*, **93**, 24–38.

ST. GEORGE, R. C. C. (1952). The interplay of light and heat in the bleaching of rhodopsin. *J. gen. Physiol.*, **35**, 495–517.

SCHNEIDER, E. E., GOODEVE, C. F. and LYTHGOE, R. J. (1939). The spectral variation of the photosensitivity of visual purple. *Proc. roy. Soc. A.*, **170**, 102–112.

SMITH, E. L. and PICKELS, E. G. (1940). Micelle formation in aqueous solutions of digitonin. *Proc. nat. Acad. Sci. Wash.*, **26**, 272–277.

TRENDELENBURG, W. (1904). Quantitative Untersuchungen über die Bleichung des Sehpurpurs in Monochromatischen Licht. *Z. Psychol. Physiol. Sinnesorg.*, **37**, 1–55.

TRENDELENBURG, W. (1911). Die Objectiv feststellbaren Lichtwirkungen an der Netzhaut. *Ergebn. Physiol.*, **11**, 1–40.

WALD, G. and BROWN, P. K. (1953). The molar extinction of rhodopsin. *J. gen. Physiol.*, **37**, 189–200.

WALD, G., DURELL, J. and ST. GEORGE, R. C. C. (1950). The light reaction in the bleaching of rhodopsin. *Science*, **111**, 179–181.

WEALE, R. A. (1949a). Absorption spectra, molecular weights and visual purple. *Nature, Lond.*, **163**, 916–917.

WEALE, R. A. (1949b). Absorption spectra, molecular weights and visual purple. *Nature, London.*, **164**, 959–960.

CHAPTER FOUR

The Structure of Visual Purple (Rhodopsin)

Visual purple has not yet been obtained in the crystalline state. Indeed it is very doubtful whether pure solid specimens have ever been prepared. Normally the pigment is studied in digitonin solution and it is a difficult enough matter to ensure that such preparations are free from impurities which absorb light; to say nothing of those which do not. The amount of the colourless digitonin present, for example, is much greater than that of the visual pigment. No simple solvent for visual purple is known. It will not dissolve in water or petroleum hydrocarbons and is destroyed by such solvents as alcohol, acetone and chloroform.

Because of these difficulties and the fact that only very small amounts of visual purple can be obtained from a reasonable number of eyes, the usual chemical methods employed in working out formulae have only a limited application. Nevertheless by ingenious arguments from diverse data, and a leavening of inspired guesswork, good progress has been made.

Visual purple is a chromoprotein, that is its molecule consists of a protein to which is attached one or more chromophores (i.e. molecular groups having the property of absorbing visible light). In this respect visual purple is similar to such substances as haemoglobin, cytochrome C, haemocyanin, ovoverdin, and so on. In a chromoprotein it is normally the chromophore which is the reactive part of the molecule, the protein acting mainly as a support. For example, in haemoglobin the chromophore haeme is the carrier of oxygen. Similarly with visual purple the chromophore is responsible for the A- and B-absorption bands in the 'visible' spectrum and is the initial site of photochemical change. In most chromoproteins the chromophore structure includes a metal—usually iron or copper. Visual purple, however, is free from heavy metals and consequently is more closely related to such chromoproteins as ovoverdin and yellow

96

ferment, the chromophores of which are based on the carotenoids astaxanthene and flavin, respectively.

Visual purple solutions of a high standard of purity have now been prepared, notably by WALD (1949) and by COLLINS, LOVE and MORTON (1952). The density spectrum of visual purple (Fig. 4.1) is characterized by three bands. The most important of these is the

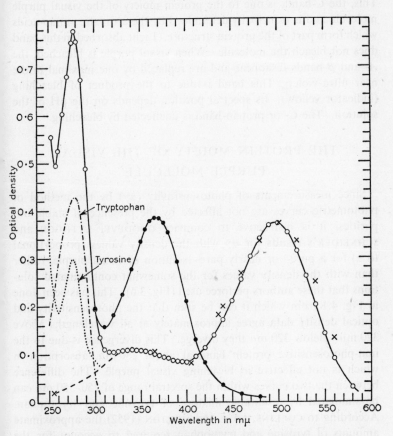

FIG. 4.1. Analysis of the density spectrum of visual purple. O O O, density spectrum of a pure solution of cattle visual purple (pH 9·2); ● ● ●, ditto after bleaching (the C-band is unaffected); × × × Goodeve, Lythgoe and Schneider's photosensitivity data for frog visual purple, equated at 500 mμ to the density spectrum. The non-photosensitive C-band can be accounted for by tyrosine and tryptophan, as indicated.

(*Modified after Collins, Love and Morton,* 1952)

A-band, maximal at about 500 mμ. After descending to a minimum at about 400 mμ the spectrum rises again to a small peak—the B-band—at about 350 mμ. Absorption in this band, as GOODEVE, LYTHGOE and SCHNEIDER's results showed (Chap. 3) is also effective in bleaching visual purple. Beyond the B-band in the ultra-violet the spectrum again rises to a sharp, high maximum at about 278 mμ. This, the C-band, is due to the protein moiety of the visual purple molecule and is principally determined by the aromatic amino-acids which form part of the protein structure. Light absorbed in this band does not bleach the molecule. When visual purple is bleached, the A- and B-bands disappear and are replaced by one maximal in the near ultra-violet. This band is due to the product of bleaching (indicator yellow): its spectral position depends on the pH of the solution. The C- or protein-band is unaffected by bleaching.

THE PROTEIN MOIETY OF THE VISUAL PURPLE MOLECULE

Since measurements of photosensitivity ($\alpha\gamma$) by the method of photometric curves are not affected by the presence of stable impurities, it is instructive to compare GOODEVE, LYTHGOE and SCHNEIDER's results for $\alpha\gamma$ with the density values (proportional to α) for a pure—or nearly pure—solution of visual purple, rather than with the density values for the somewhat contaminated solutions that these authors perforce used (Fig. 3·6). This has been done in Fig. 4.1 from which it can be seen that the photosensitivity and optical density data agree approximately at all wavelengths above 320 mμ. Below 320 mμ they diverge. This divergence is due to the non-photosensitive protein band at about 280 mμ, absorption in which is not effective in bleaching visual purple. The difference between the two curves within the spectral range of 250–350 mμ can be simulated by a suitable mixture of tyrosine and tryptophan. According to COLLINS, LOVE and MORTON (1952) the approximate amounts of tyrosine and tryptophan required to account for the protein band are 6 per cent and 3 per cent, respectively, of the dry weight of visual purple. These percentages are normal for animal proteins, e.g. casein (6·6 and 1·2), haemoglobin (3·2 and 1·3) and cattle fibrin (6·5 and 3·0). The whole density spectrum of visual purple within the wavelength range of 250–600 mμ can thus be accounted for in terms of that due to the photosensitive chromophore (*A*- and *B*-bands at *c*. 500 mμ and 350 mμ, respectively) and that due to protein (*C*-band at 280 mμ).

The nature of the protein moiety probably varies from species to species. Such variation might account for the slight differences, observed in different animals, for the wavelength position of the *A*-band maximum. For example frog's visual purple has an *A*-band maximum at 502–503 mμ; rat, ox and sheep visual purples at 498–500 mμ (COLLINS and MORTON, 1950a); human visual purple at 497 mμ (CRESCITELLI and DARTNALL, 1953).

THE CHROMOPHORE OF THE VISUAL PURPLE MOLECULE

Of more immediate interest is the structure of the chromophore group and the nature of its linkage to the protein moiety. Information about this has come mainly from a study of the simpler breakdown products of visual purple.

THE VISUAL PIGMENTS AND THEIR BREAKDOWN PRODUCTS, THE RETINENES AND VITAMINS A

WALD (see Chap. 2) showed that the chromophore of visual purple is related to the carotenoids, a large class of fat-soluble, highly unsaturated pigments found in animals and plants. According to WALD (1949): 'when rhodopsin is exposed to light in the retina, two major changes occur; the carotenoid is cleaved from protein, and is degraded through orange intermediates, first to the yellow retinene$_1$, then to colourless vitamin A$_1$. The retina can also re-synthesize rhodopsin in two ways: rapidly by reversion from retinene$_1$, and relatively slowly from vitamin A$_1$.' Porphyropsin (or visual violet) the photosensitive pigment of fresh-water fish was shown by WALD to be similarly related to corresponding substances, retinene$_2$ and vitamin A$_2$. The absorption spectra of the visual pigments (in 1 per cent aqueous digitonin) and of their corresponding retinenes and vitamins A (in chloroform) are shown in Fig. 2.2.

The structural formula for vitamin A$_1$ (C$_{19}$H$_{27}$.CH$_2$OH) is or, in more convenient shorthand,

It is, therefore, a polyene alcohol, i.e. is characterized by a regular alternation of double and single valency bonds in the molecule—a feature common to all the carotenoids. In chloroform solution, vitamin A_1 has a single absorption band in the ultraviolet ($\lambda_{max} = 332$ mμ) and, when mixed with antimony trichloride reagent, gives a transient blue colour ($\lambda_{max} = 620$ mμ). Retinene$_1$ has a single absorption band in the near ultra-violet ($\lambda_{max} = 385$ mμ in chloroform) and, like vitamin A_1, also yields a blue colour ($\lambda_{max} = 664$ mμ) with antimony trichloride.

The probable structural formula for vitamin A_2 ($C_{19}H_{25}.CH_2OH$), the corresponding decomposition product of visual violet (porphyropsin) is,

i.e. the ring structure contains one conjugated double bond more than that of vitamin A_1.

RELATIONSHIP BETWEEN ABSORPTION SPECTRA AND STRUCTURE IN THE CONJUGATED POLYENES

In the structural formulae of organic chemistry each single valency bond is equivalent to two electrons, more or less equally shared between the two atoms forming the bond. Similarly a double bond is equivalent to four shared electrons.

Where there is a conjugated chain of alternate single and double bonds, however, a special situation arises. For example, the formula for the conjugated fragment,

could equally well be written

provided the groups to which the ends of the chain were attached would permit such a rearrangement of valencies. In such cases the molecule could exist in two structural states. Some molecules would be in one state, some in the other. Some (perhaps the majority) would be neither in one nor the other but in some intermediate condition represented by

in which the black dots represent unpaired electrons.

According to modern ideas the electrons which remain (five in the present example), after allocation of a single bond linkage between each adjacent atom, mutually interact to form so-called π-orbitals. These are not limited to the space separating adjacent atoms but extend over the whole length of the conjugated chain. Several π-orbitals can occur, much as a violin string can vibrate in several modes to give harmonics in addition to the fundamental note. In the unexcited state the electrons occupy orbitals of lowest energy, but, on absorption of a quantum of suitable magnitude, they enter orbitals of higher energy. By the exclusion principle of Pauli only one electron (of a given spin) can occupy each orbital. As the conjugated chain increases in length the number of π-electrons increases also. Consequently more of the ground-state orbitals are filled and less energy (i.e. a quantum of lower frequency) is required to raise an electron to the next higher orbital—the incremental energy of successive orbitals being progressively smaller. Thus in simple conjugated systems the energy required is so great that absorption occurs only in the ultra-violet, where the frequency (and hence the quantal energy) is sufficiently large. In systems of greater conjugation, the necessary activation energy is smaller and may be supplied by a quantum in the 'visible' range. Thus in the diphenyl polyenes,

the simplest members ($n = 1$ and 2) absorb in the ultra-violet and are colourless but, as n is increased the spectral location of the absorption band advances towards the visible, and the subsequent members are coloured. Thus when $n = 3$, the compound is pale yellow; when $n = 5$, it is orange; when $n = 11$ it is violet and when $n = 15$ it is green—the absorption bands being centred respectively in the violet, blue, green and red regions of the spectrum.

Roughly speaking the addition of one conjugated ethylene group (—CH=CH—) to poleyene structures causes a shift in the density spectrum of about 20–25 mμ towards longer wavelengths. Now vitamin A_1, which has an absorption maximum at about 330 mμ, has five conjugated double bonds, while retinene$_1$ which has, in addition, a conjugated carbonyl group (—C=O) has its maximum at 380 mμ. The A-band of visual purple is maximal at 500 mμ, i.e. 120 mμ further on. To account for this shift in terms of an increase in length of the conjugated chain would require the addition of 5–6 double bonds, equivalent to the addition of another vitamin A_1 structure.

Arguing along these lines WALD (1949) suggested that the chromophore of visual purple was derived from two molecules of vitamin A_1 or retinene$_1$. Similarly, the chromophore of visual violet (porphyropsin) was supposed to be derived from two molecules of vitamin A_2 or retinene$_2$.

Now the vitamin A_2 molecule contains one conjugated bond more than vitamin A_1. This would account for the displacement of its density spectrum to longer wavelengths. But the difference in spectral position between the rhodopsin and porphyropsin bands is no greater than the separation of the bands of retinene$_1$ and retinene$_2$, or of vitamin A_1 and vitamin A_2 (Fig. 2.2). If the visual pigments were derived from two molecules of vitamin A one would expect a difference between them, corresponding to two conjugated double bonds.

A further difficulty is the fact that in nearly all the carotenoids—which are based on a 'double vitamin A' structure—the main absorption band is characterized by three or more sharp subsidiary peaks.

An exception to this general rule is the carotenoid astacene which, like visual purple, has a single smooth absorption band in the visible.

The spectra of astacene and visual purple are compared in Fig. 4.2. Although both spectra have a maximum at c. 500 mμ and are of similar shapes, that for astacene is roughly twice the height of that for visual purple. Since astacene has a 'double vitamin A' structure this suggests that the visual purple chromophore contains only one molecule of vitamin A.

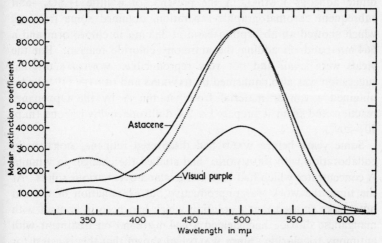

FIG. 4.2. Comparison of the density spectra of astacene (in pyridine) with that of visual purple (in digitonin solution). The dotted curve gives the density spectrum of visual purple equated at 500 mμ to that for astacene.

In a recent molecular weight determination (see Chap. 3, p. 94), HUBBARD (1954) has shown that the molecule of cattle visual purple contains a single chromophore based on one C_{20} unit.

THE RELATIONSHIP BETWEEN RETINENE$_1$
AND VITAMIN A$_1$

A considerable step forward was made when it was found that retinene$_1$ is the aldehyde of vitamin A$_1$

retinene$_1$ (vitamin A$_1$ aldehyde)
$C_{19}H_{27}\cdot CHO$

MORTON (1944) had come to this conclusion purely from a consideration of absorption spectra. The problem was how to prove it, by converting vitamin A_1 to retinene$_1$. This involved oxidation of the alcohol group to aldehyde without affecting the vulnerable double bonds in the molecule. MORTON and GOODWIN (1944), by shaking vitamin A concentrates, dissolved in light petroleum, with dilute aqueous $KMnO_4$ in the presence of a little H_2SO_4—and subsequent chromatographic separation, obtained some fractions which showed an absorption band at 385 mμ in chloroform and a 664 mμ band on adding the antimony chloride reagent. But the yields were small and not very reproducible. MORTON'S original suggestion was also confirmed by HAWKINS and HUNTER (1944) who obtained a similar material from vitamin A by the Oppenauer reaction and from it prepared a 2,4 dinitrophenylhydrazone (m.p. 207–209°).

Some years before WALD had discovered retinene, MORTON, in collaboration with DRUMMOND, had studied the changes in vitamin A concentrates which had been left to stand over various solids. At the time, the work was unproductive but examination of the old notebooks showed that a solution which had been in contact with manganese dioxide had yielded a 664 mμ band on treatment with antimony trichloride. Since WALD had shown that this is a test for retinene$_1$, 'the old observations slipped into a pattern.' BALL, GOODWIN and MORTON (1948) therefore dissolved vitamin A concentrates in light petroleum, added manganese dioxide and allowed the mixture to stand 6–10 days in darkness. Almost quantitative yields of a substance giving the same colour reaction ($\lambda_{max} = 664$ mμ with antimony trichloride reagent) as retinene$_1$ were obtained. They crystallized the synthetic retinene (m.p. 61–62°C) and on analysis found C 84·2 per cent, H 9·76 per cent; molecular weight 236 ($C_{19}H_{27}CHO$ requires C 84·5, H 9·85 per cent, mol. wt. 284). Derivatives of retinene (the 2,4 dinitrophenylhydrazone, the semicarbazone and the hydrazone) were prepared, and these analysed according to expectations though (as in the case of synthetic retinene itself) the molecular weights—determined by depression of freezing point of camphene using Rast's micro method—were rather low.

THE RELATIONSHIP BETWEEN RETINENE$_1$ AND INDICATOR YELLOW

Synthetic retinene$_1$, prepared by oxidizing vitamin A_1 to its aldehyde by manganese dioxide (BALL, GOODWIN and MORTON,

1948) appears to be identical with the natural retinene$_1$ which can be extracted from bleached visual purple solutions by a mixed solvent consisting of acetone, ethanol and light petroleum. Thus, in chloroform, both synthetic and natural retinene$_1$ have density maxima at 380–385 mμ and both give the same colour test ($\lambda_{max} = 664$) with the antimony trichloride reagent.

When synthetic retinene$_1$ is dissolved in 1 per cent aqueous digitonin its density spectrum ($\lambda_{max} = 380$ mμ) is not affected by pH.

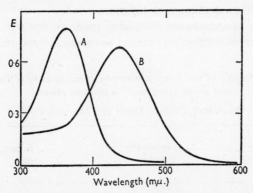

FIG. 4.3. Imitation of the reactions of indicator yellow. Curve A, density spectrum of compound formed by the reaction of retinene$_1$ and methylamine in alkaline solution; curve B, the same after acidification.

(*Ball, Collins, Dalvi and Morton*, 1949)

The density spectrum of a bleached visual purple solution, on the other hand, is dependent on the pH: in alkaline solution the colour is pale yellow whilst in acid solution it is deep chrome yellow. LYTHGOE (1937) gave the name 'indicator yellow' to the substance responsible for these changes. Indicator yellow has $\lambda_{max} = 365$ mμ in alkaline solution and $\lambda_{max} = 440$ mμ in acid solution.

The probable relationship between retinene$_1$ and indicator yellow has now been established by the brilliant investigations of MORTON and his colleagues at Liverpool (BALL, COLLINS, MORTON and STUBBS, 1948; BALL, COLLINS, DALVI and MORTON, 1949; COLLINS, 1953). These authors studied the interaction between retinene$_1$ and amino compounds. The procedure was to mix an aqueous solution of the amino compound with an alcoholic solution of crystalline retinene$_1$ and then to add 0·1 N caustic soda solution. After allowing the mixture to stand for 15–30 min its density spectrum was measured. The solution was then acidified (with one drop of concentrated hydrochloric acid in order to avoid gross changes in concentration) and its density spectrum measured again. The results of a typical experiment are shown in Fig. 4.3. Curve A shows the density spectrum of the compound formed by retinene$_1$ and methylamine (CH_3—NH_2) in alkaline solution. This compound has a maximum at 360–365 mμ. Curve B shows the density spectrum after acidification. This has a maximum at 435 mμ.

A number of compounds containing amino groups were tried (see table). When interaction between the amino-compound and retinene$_1$

Wavelengths of maximum absorption of mixtures of retinene$_1$ and amino compounds in aqueous ethanol

(from Ball, Collins, Dalvi and Morton, 1949)

Amino compound	λ_{max} in alkali (mμ)	λ_{max} in acid (mμ)
Methylamine	360–365	435
Dimethylamine	385–390	385–390 (no change)
Benzylamine	365	445
Urea	385–390	385–390 (no change)
Formamide	385–390	385–390 (no change)
Glycine	372	440–445
β-Alanine	365	440
Serine	370	435–455
Isoleucine	370	450–455
Tyrosine	365	445
Tryptophan	360–365	445
Glutamic acid	375	435–440
Lysine	365	440–445
Arginine	365–370	460
Egg albumin	370	450
Peptone	365	440
Edestin	380	455
Trypsin	Solution not clear	440–450
Gelatin	360	440
Casein	360	Orange yellow precipitate
Zein	360–365	Orange yellow precipitate

took place, the alkaline solutions had an absorption band maximum at 360–370 mμ. On acidification, this band was replaced by another having its maximum at 435–460 mμ. When no reaction occurred (i.e. with dimethylamine, urea and formamide) the solutions showed merely the characteristic band of uncombined retinene$_1$ (λ_{max} = 385–390 mμ); this was unaffected by pH.

Although a large excess of amino compound over retinene$_1$ was required in these experiments the authors considered that the reaction must involve two molecules of retinene$_1$ to one of the amine 'since one molecule of retinene$_1$ with one molecule of aliphatic amine could scarcely give the indicator yellow type of spectrum. This implies that conjugated proteins resembling and including indicator yellow itself possess two retinene$_1$ molecules attached to the same amino nitrogen atom.' (BALL, COLLINS, DALVI and MORTON, 1949.)

As a result of this work, COLLINS and MORTON (1950b) suggested the following as the most likely formula for the condensation product of retinene$_1$ and methylamine in alkaline solution.

In this formulation there is a break in the conjugation at the N-group and the structure, having two sets of *six* conjugated double bonds, may be compared with two unconjugated vitamin A$_2$ residues (λ_{max} = 350 mμ). Addition of acid would then give

with 'full' conjugation restored.

The first structure corresponds to alkaline indicator yellow and might be expected to have an absorption band maximum at 365 mμ. The second structure corresponds to acid indicator yellow with λ_{max} at 440 mμ.

The methylamine-retinene$_1$ compound was, of course, proposed only as an analogue to indicator yellow. In the latter substance the protein was supposed to be attached to the central nitrogen atom in place of the methyl (—CH$_3$) group.

COLLINS and MORTON (1950c) supposed the conversion of visual purple to indicator yellow to be an oxidative process involving the loss of two electrons. Accordingly, they proposed the following structural formula for the visual purple chromophore,

one of at least twelve resonance forms, the most probable being those with the negative change on the carbon atoms adjacent to the nitrogen atom.

In 1953, however, COLLINS, referring to unpublished work by COLLINS, MORTON, PITT and STOK, reported that the compound formed by interaction between retinene and methylamine was, in fact, a 'Schiff's base' with the formula,

and not the product of one amino group with two retinene molecules as at first had been thought. This substance, retinene methylimine, was obtained in the crystalline state, m.p. 73°C. It had an absorption maximum at 365 mμ in ethyl alcohol, a molecular weight (Rast's method using camphene) of 290 and contained 4·82 per cent nitrogen ($C_{19}H_{27}CH = N—CH_3$ requires M.W. = 297, 4·71 per cent N). On acidification a substance with $\lambda_{max} = 440$ mμ in ethyl alcohol was obtained. This analogue of acid indicator yellow could not be crystallized. The best preparation had m.p. = 140°C and contained 3·9 per cent nitrogen. The hydrochloride of retinene methylimine, $C_{19}H_{27}CH = \overset{+}{N}HCH_3\}\overset{-}{Cl}$, requires 4·2 per cent N, in fair agreement with the experimental figure. However, COLLINS (1953) considered that a substance of this formula would have an absorption maximum at a wavelength similar to that for the free imine (365 mμ) and that the observed position (440 mμ) implied a doubled molecule for the acid form. This seems to be an unnecessary hypothesis for the λ_{max} position might well shift as a result of the positive charge carried by the nitrogen atom in the hydrochloride formula. A molecular weight determination would help to settle the matter, but in the meantime it would seem that the most likely formulations for the alkaline and acid forms of the indicator yellow analogues prepared by the Liverpool group are:

$$\lambda_{max} = 360\text{–}370 \text{ m}\mu \qquad\qquad \lambda_{max} = 435\text{–}460 \text{ m}\mu$$

Analogue of alkaline indicator yellow   Analogue of acid indicator yellow

where R is protein in the case of true indicator yellow.

IS THE STRUCTURE OF INDICATOR YELLOW A CLUE TO THE STRUCTURE OF VISUAL PURPLE?

According to WALD (1938) LYTHGOE'S pH-sensitive indicator yellow is 'a mixture of retinene$_1$ and protein, about two-thirds still loosely attached to each other.' WALD states (1949) that when visual purple is bleached in the retina 'the carotenoid is cleaved from protein.' He regards indicator yellow as an unimportant pheno-menon of visual purple *solutions* and certainly not a part of the visual cycle *in vivo*. In their 1948 paper, BALL, COLLINS, MORTON and STUBBS were apparently of the same opinion. Struck by the fact that indicator yellow analogues could be prepared by the interaction of retinene$_1$ and many amino compounds (see table, p. 106) they con-sidered that 'the conclusion to be drawn concerning "indicator yellow" is that free or loosely bound retinene$_1$ (the final product of bleaching rhodopsin) may combine with any suitable protein or amino-acid which may be available. In that case "indicator yellow" would be a fortuitous artefact having no direct relevance to visual chemistry, and WALD'S cycle connecting vitamin A retinene and rhodopsin need not be complicated by trying to fit in indicator yellow.'

This view was questioned by DARTNALL (1948) who referred to LYTHGOE'S (1937) inability to extract retinene from bleached visual purple solutions using the bland petroleum ether alone as solvent and to the statement by HECHT (1942) that in order to extract the retinene the active agent alcohol must be added to petroleum ether. HECHT had also observed that if cold acetone is added to a bleached visual purple solution the precipitate 'contains not only the protein but most of the yellow colour. The retinene must therefore still be mainly attached to the protein since carotenoids are not easily adsorbed in the presence of high concentrations of acetone' (HECHT, 1942). From these facts DARTNALL inferred that after bleaching, the altered visual purple chromophore was still attached to the parent protein, this arrangement constituting the indicator yellow molecule.

In reply, BALL, COLLINS and MORTON (1948) stated that 'if under the action of light retinene is split off, the conditions are such that it is available for recombination with any protein to form new compounds.' Spectroscopic evidence showed that there were three materials in bleached visual purple solutions, namely, retinene (or retinene 'loosely bound to protein') and the acid and alkaline forms of indicator yellow. In their opinion the same protein was concerned in all three compounds, the chemical evidence suggesting that, in indicator yellow, the retinene was firmly bound but in neutral bleached visual purple solutions only weakly bound.

BLISS (1948) suggested that the reason why LYTHGOE had been unable to extract retinene from bleached visual purple solution was 'because he did not shake his extract with enough vigour to compensate for the slow diffusion of the liberated retinene through the aqueous phase to the petroleum ether.' However, in support of the view that retinene is not split from the visual purple molecule by light, he pointed out that even in the presence of an active agent such as alcohol, retinene is not extracted by petroleum ether for a period of 2–10 min after the solution has been bleached (BLISS, 1948). BLISS also recalled LYTHGOE'S (1937) observation of the two forms of acid indicator yellow: a stable form ($\lambda_{max} = 450$ mμ) at pH's less than 4 and an unstable form ($\lambda_{max} = 445$ mμ) at pH's between 4 and 6. The unstable form of acid indicator yellow readily releases retinene when its solutions are shaken with petroleum ether and BLISS supposed that this form corresponded to the 'loosely bound retinene' mentioned by BALL, COLLINS and MORTON.

The above discussion has been reproduced in some detail because it illustrates the different views held then, and to some extent even now. At the time (1948) it seemed that the question at issue was: indicator yellow *or* retinene? When it should have been: which comes first?—a situation only imperfectly grasped (except, perhaps by BLISS).

However, COLLINS and MORTON (1950b) soon devised tests to

ascertain the answer. BALL, COLLINS, DALVI and MORTON (1949) had shown that retinene would readily react with p-aminobenzoic acid to give a substance (not an indicator yellow analogue) which had an absorption maximum at 535 mμ. COLLINS and MORTON therefore carried out the following four experiments. p-aminobenzoic acid in excess was added (1) to a freshly bleached, slightly acid visual purple solution and the mixture was made first alkaline and then acid; (2) to a slightly acid unbleached visual purple solution, which was then bleached, made alkaline and finally acid; (3) to a freshly bleached neutral visual purple solution, which was then acidified; (4) to a neutral unbleached visual purple solution, which was then bleached and made acid. In all cases results were negative, i.e. no band at 535 mμ appeared. This indicated that there was no free retinene in the solutions immediately after bleaching. Again, retinene will combine with proteins or aliphatic amines (to form indicator yellow analogues) only if the solutions are alkaline. If retinene were formed before indicator yellow then, on bleaching an *acid* solution of visual purple, one would expect to obtain only free retinene ($\lambda_{max} = 385$ mμ); not acid indicator yellow ($\lambda_{max} = 440$ mμ) as is, in fact, produced. From these results COLLINS and MORTON deduced that indicator yellow is formed first and may then be either wholly or partly converted to retinene. They concluded that 'the structure of indicator yellow is of vital importance to the structure of rhodopsin. It is clear that although transient orange is the primary product of irradiation, indicator yellow is the first reasonably stable product. The original attachment between carrier protein and chromophoric groups is clearly unbroken and the C—N link of the indicator yellow must also occur in rhodopsin.' (COLLINS and MORTON (1950).)

Strong confirmatory evidence for this conclusion has recently been advanced by COLLINS (1953). His argument runs as follows. Although, when acid solutions of visual purple are bleached, indicator yellow is formed, it might, perhaps, be argued (taking the opposite view that retinene is the first stable product of bleaching) that freshly-formed retinene is in an activated state and in this condition might then react with protein to form indicator yellow, even though the conditions were acid.

If retinene is formed first, then it ought to be possible—by 'blocking' all amino groups in the unbleached visual purple molecules—to prevent the subsequent formation of indicator yellow. One way of doing this is by the use of formaldehyde which reacts with amino groups as follows:

$$R—\overset{+}{N}H_3 \rightleftarrows R—NH_2 + H^+$$
$$R—NH_2 + HCHO \rightleftarrows R—NH(CH_2OH)$$
$$R—NH(CH_2OH) + HCHO \rightleftarrows R—N(CH_2OH)_2$$

Since these reactions are all reversible it is not possible to ensure that all free amino groups are blocked. A state of equilibrium will be set up in which a proportion (depending on conditions) will be blocked and the remainder will be free.

To ensure that in a visual purple solution to which formaldehyde had been added the proportion of the free amino groups was not underestimated COLLINS assumed that all amino groups were in the form of tyrosine (the amino acid with the least affinity for formaldehyde). According to LEVY and SILBERMAN (1937), if a solution of tyrosine is made 10 molar in formaldehyde and the pH adjusted to 9, the proportion of free tyrosine ($R—\overset{+}{N}H_3$ or $R—NH_2$) to combined ($R—NH(CH_2OH)$ or $R—N(CH_2OH)_2$) is 0·0036.

Solutions of visual purple which were 13×10^{-6} molar in respect of retinene were found to contain 3 micrograms of amino-nitrogen per millilitre. To be on the safe side, COLLINS assumed an upper limit of 5 micrograms per millilitre which is equivalent to 360×10^{-6} molar. If now, to such a solution, formaldehyde is added so that the final mixture is 10 molar in formaldehyde, and the pH is adjusted to 9, then the concentration of free amino groups when equilibrium is established will be $0·0036 \times 360 \times 10^{-6}$ molar $= 1·3 \times 10^{-6}$ molar. Since the potential concentration of retinene in the bleached solution is 13×10^{-6} molar this means that at most, only 10 per cent can combine with protein to form indicator yellow. On the other hand, if the C—N link in visual purple is unbroken on bleaching, then the previous blocking of free amino-groups will not affect the amount of indicator yellow, which, accordingly, should approach 100 per cent.

There is, however, an additional complication. If retinene methylimine (an analogue of indicator yellow) is dissolved in water with the aid of a 'solubilizer,' and the pH adjusted to 9·3, the absorption maximum changes from 363 mμ (cf. alkaline indicator yellow) to 380 mμ (free retinene). This hydrolysis is a monomolecular reaction with a half-period of 25 min at 18°C. In the case of indicator yellow, a similar hydrolysis to retinene and protein would be expected.

In one experiment, 1 ml of visual purple solution was mixed with 3 ml of 40 per cent formaldehyde to which buffer had been added to bring the pH to 9. The optical density of the solution at 500 mμ was 0·760. The solution was then bleached with intense light. The

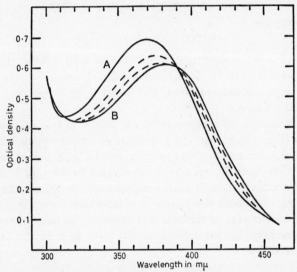

FIG. 4.4. The hydrolysis of alkaline indicator yellow to retinene at pH 9 in the presence of 10 M formaldehyde. Curve *A*, density spectrum of freshly bleached visual purple solution; dashed curves, later measurements; curve *B*, after 60 min.

(*Redrawn after Collins*, 1953)

difference in density at 500 mμ before and after bleaching was 0·728. Taking the molecular extinction coefficient of retinene as 48,000, these measurements show that the solution of visual purple was $15·2 \times 10^{-6}$ molar in potential retinene. Immediately after bleaching, the density spectrum of the solution was measured at frequent intervals, for an hour, over the range 300–460 mμ. The results (Fig. 4.4) showed a well-defined isosbestic point indicating the transformation of one substance into another. The final density spectrum (curve *B*, Fig. 4.4) corresponds closely to free retinene, the first spectrum (curve *A*, Fig. 4.4) to a mixture of retinene and alkaline indicator yellow. The molecular extinction coefficient (aqueous) of retinene at 360 mμ is 28,200 while that of alkaline indicator yellow is 50,000. If x is the concentration of retinene at a time t after bleaching and y, that of indicator yellow, then the final concentration of retinene will be $x + y$. Thus using the values at 360 mμ in Fig. 4.4

$$(\text{Curve } A)\ 28{,}200x + 50{,}000y + i = 0{\cdot}676$$

where i is absorption due to impurities and

$$(\text{Curve } B)\ 28{,}200(x + y) + i = 0{\cdot}543.$$

By subtraction,

$$y(50{,}000 - 28{,}000) = 0{\cdot}133,$$

whence $y = 6{\cdot}1 \times 10^{-6}$ molar, i.e. 40 per cent of the potential retinene ($15{\cdot}2 \times 10^{-6}$). In another similar experiment y, the initial indicator yellow concentration, was found to be 49 per cent of the potential retinene.

The hydrolysis of alkaline indicator yellow to free retinene and protein (Fig. 4.4) is, like the hydrolysis of retinene methylimine, a monomolecular reaction but with a shorter half period, namely 9 min. Consequently, since 5–10 min elapsed between the beginning of irradiation and the first density measurement at 360 mμ, the initial concentration of indicator yellow must have been a good deal higher than 40–49 per cent of the potential retinene. In fact, immediately after bleaching, all the retinene could have been in the form of indicator yellow.

VIEWS OF THE HARVARD SCHOOL ON THE STRUCTURE OF RHODOPSIN (VISUAL PURPLE)

INDICATOR YELLOW

In the preceding arguments concerning the structure of visual purple (rhodopsin), indicator yellow has occupied a key position. Recently the Harvard school (WALD and his colleagues) have made tentative observations on the structure of rhodopsin, and in doing so have denied the relevance of indicator yellow. Before describing the experiments on which they base their proposals for the rhodopsin structure, it is necessary, therefore, to study their views on indicator yellow.

In a recent paper, WALD and HUBBARD (1949) wrote 'the retinene$_1$-protein which results from bleaching rhodopsin in solution is almost colourless when alkaline and bright yellow when acid (CHASE, 1936).

114

For this reason LYTHGOE called it "indicator yellow." We find its absorption maxima to lie at about 366 mμ at pH 9–9·5, 387 mμ at pH 6·7–7 and 393 mμ at pH 4–4·5.'

Now LYTHGOE's indicator yellow is the substance, present in freshly bleached rhodopsin solutions, which has λ_{max} at 365 mμ in alkaline solution and 440 mμ in acid solution. Of the acid form of LYTHGOE's indicator yellow, WALD and HUBBARD (*ibid.*) write 'when rhodopsin is bleached at pH about 4 this material appears as an initial product. In light or darkness the 440 mμ maximum slowly moves towards shorter wavelengths, finally coming to rest at about 390 mμ, the maximum of acidic retinene$_1$ (WALD, 1938). The 440 mμ material therefore is not acidic retinene$_1$-protein but its precursor; and so is homologous with the 480 mμ precursor of retinene$_1$ in neutral solution. In LYTHGOE's terminology it should be regarded as part of the "transient orange" complex, not as the acidic form of "indicator yellow".'

The suggestion that acid indicator yellow ($\lambda_{max} = 440$ mμ) is transient orange ($\lambda_{max} = 480$ mμ) in an acid medium cannot be accepted. LYTHGOE himself (1937) had clearly thought of this as a possibility and had devised an experiment to test it. He first bleached an alkaline solution of rhodopsin to the indicator yellow stage (i.e. all transient orange had decomposed to alkaline indicator yellow). On making this solution acid, the 440 mμ chromogen (acid indicator yellow) was formed. It might, perhaps, be argued that acidification had restored the transient orange. If so, then on making the solution alkaline once more one would expect the reappearance of the 480 mμ maximum. This, however, does not happen; the absorption spectrum of the solution reverts to that for alkaline indicator yellow. 'The change can be repeated any number of times' (LYTHGOE, 1937).

Both acid and alkaline forms of indicator yellow eventually suffer hydrolysis to form retinene ($\lambda_{max} = 385$ mμ) and protein. Through confusing acid indicator yellow ($\lambda_{max} = 440$ mμ) with transient orange, WALD and HUBBARD were led to believe that the λ_{max} for acid indicator yellow is at 390 mμ, the value for a faded solution in which the indicator yellow had been largely hydrolysed to retinene and protein.

REGENERATION OF RHODOPSIN

WALD and BROWN (1950) found that solutions of retinene$_1$ and 'opsin' (the protein of rhodopsin) will react spontaneously in darkness to form rhodopsin in good yield. Opsin was prepared, e.g. from cattle retinae, in the following way. The retinae were removed and bleached to the colourless condition by exposure to light. The outer segments of the rods were then separated from the rest of the retina by flotation in 45 per cent sucrose solution. This was then diluted. The bleached outer segments were centrifuged out, washed, and extracted with 2 per cent digitonin solution.

The synthesis of rhodopsin from $retinene_1$ and opsin is inhibited by 0·1 M hydroxylamine. This is because hydroxylamine condenses with $retinene_1$ to form an oxime, and thus acts in competition with opsin for the aldehyde group in the $retinene_1$ molecule. The synthesis of rhodopsin is likewise inhibited by 0·7 M formaldehyde. In this case, however, the aldehyde group of formaldehyde competes with that of $retinene_1$ for those groups in the opsin molecule which are involved in the reaction.

Now the work of MORTON and his colleagues had suggested that in the formation of indicator yellow, and hence of rhodopsin, retinene reacts with an amino group. However, aldehydes will also readily react with sulph-hydryl (—SH) groups. WALD and BROWN (1952) therefore proceeded to consider which of these alternative reactions would provide a basis for the synthesis of rhodopsin.

In solutions more acid than pH 6–7, amino groups exist mainly in the form of ammonium ions ($-\overset{+}{N}H_3$), which do not readily react with aldehydes. Thus MORTON and co-workers had found that the reaction between aliphatic amino compounds and retinene took place only in alkaline solution (p. 105), and even then only slowly unless the amino compound was present in excess. Sulph-hydryl groups, on the other hand, remain unionized up to about pH 8–9 and only in more alkaline solutions are they ionized (—S⁻). At lower pH's, sulph-hydryl groups readily react with formaldehyde and other aldehydes.

WALD and BROWN therefore investigated the regeneration of rhodopsin, from $retinene_1$ and opsin, over a wide pH range. In their experiments 0·5 ml of a rhodopsin solution was mixed in the dark with 0·25 ml of a concentrated solution of $retinene_1$ in digitonin and with 0·25 ml of buffer or another reagent. A sample of the solution was then completely bleached by exposing it to a 160 W tungsten lamp, suitable filters being used to remove heat and ultra-violet radiation. The bleached solution was then allowed to regenerate in darkness for 2–2½ hr at 24–27°C. At the end of this period 0·1 ml of

116

a 1 M solution of freshly neutralized hydroxylamine was added, 'to prevent further regeneration and to remove fortuitous retinene$_1$ complexes.' The density spectrum before and after exposure to light was then measured. The change gave the difference spectrum of the regenerated rhodopsin. A control bleaching of another sample of the original solution to which hydroxylamine had been added gave

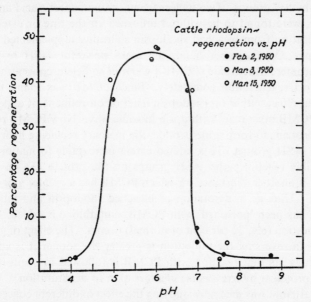

Fig. 4.5. The regeneration of cattle visual purple in bleached solutions containing added retinene$_1$. Regeneration time 2–2$\frac{1}{2}$ hr, temperature, 24–27°C.

(*Wald and Brown*, 1952)

the difference spectrum of the original rhodopsin. From these results the percentage regeneration was calculated.

The results are given by the pH-activity curve in Fig. 4.5. This shows that the optimum condition for regeneration was at pH 6. Above pH 7 and below pH 4·5, however, little regeneration occurred.

Since —NH$_2$ groups exist mainly as the non-reactive —NH$_3^+$ ions at pH's below 6–7 whereas —SH groups do not appreciably ionize at pH's below 8–9, WALD and BROWN (1952) considered that 'one can conclude from these measurements alone that the synthesis of rhodopsin is optimal at pH's which are disadvantageous for the

117

condensation of retinene$_1$ with amino groups, yet favour its condensation with sulfhydryl groups.'

INHIBITION OF REGENERATION BY SULPH-HYDRYL REAGENTS

Because of this result WALD and BROWN (1952) decided to investigate regeneration in the presence of substances which react with sulph-hydryl groups. Two such reagents, monoiodacetic acid and its amide, were found to be without influence on the rate or extent of regeneration from bleached rhodopsin solutions supplemented with retinene. On the other hand, the more powerful —SH reagent, p-chloromercuribenzoate (PCMB), when in sufficient concentration, inhibited regeneration completely. Since PCMB was found to be without effect, either on rhodopsin itself or on retinene, it appeared that PCMB must react with opsin in some way. Now PCMB reacts with proteins to form a mercaptide, the mercury replacing hydrogen in the —SH groups. To a limited extent mercaptide formation is a reversible reaction; the —SH groups on the protein can be reinstated if another substance for which PCMB has a greater affinity is added. Thus if, to a solution of bleached rhodopsin and retinene which has been 'poisoned' with PCMB, glutathione is added, some regeneration (e.g. 30 per cent of normal) occurs. The effect of glutathione in reversing the inhibition is greater the sooner it is added. This suggests that reaction with PCMB is followed in opsin (as in other proteins) by irreversible changes akin to denaturation.

An attempt was made, by studying the effect of different concentrations of PCMB to ascertain how many —SH groups took part in the synthesis of rhodopsin from retinene and opsin. It was found, however, that the lowest concentration of PCMB which completely inhibited regeneration was 10–12 mole equivalent. This suggested that the preparations contained many more —SH groups titratable with PCMB than directly participated in the linkage of retinene to opsin.

LIBERATION OF SULPH-HYDRYL GROUPS WHEN RHODOPSIN BLEACHES

In order to obtain a trustworthy figure for the number of —SH groups directly involved in the linkage of retinene$_1$ to opsin, WALD and BROWN (1952) carried out an amperometric titration of the additional —SH groups exposed when rhodopsin is bleached.

A standard mercury-mercuric iodide half cell was connected by

118

means of a salt bridge to another half cell in which a rotating platinum electrode was in contact with an ammoniacal solution (pH 9) of rhodopsin in 2 per cent digitonin. The electrical circuit was completed through a galvanometer. Silver nitrate (0·001 M) was titrated into the visual pigment solution, the galvanometer readings being recorded for each 0·1 ml increment of silver nitrate. The results of a

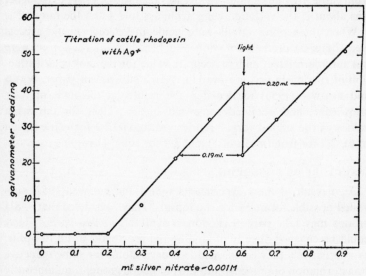

FIG. 4.6. Amperometric titration of visual purple with silver nitrate. The horizontal distances (marked 0·19 ml and 0·20 ml) give the silver ion equivalent of the sulph-hydryl groups liberated on bleaching (at the arrow labelled 'light').

(*Wald and Brown*, 1952)

typical experiment are shown in Fig. 4.6. The titration was begun in dim red light to avoid bleaching the visual pigment. No current flowed until 0·2 ml of silver nitrate solution had been added, this amount being absorbed by the free sulph-hydryl groups present in the preparation. A further 0·4 ml of silver nitrate solution was then added. This produced a linear increase of current in the circuit. The rhodopsin was then bleached by white light. The current fell (see Fig. 4.6) because the —SH groups exposed as a result of the bleaching removed silver ions from the solution. Addition of more silver nitrate ion brought the current back to its former value and beyond. From this experiment, the silver ion equivalent of the —SH groups exposed by bleaching could be measured. In the example shown (Fig. 4.6) the —SH groups were equivalent to 0·2 ml of 0·001 M solution, i.e. to 2×10^{-7} moles of —SH groups. Since the rhodopsin solution used was equivalent to $1·0 \times 10^{-7}$ moles of retinene$_1$, bleaching had released —SH groups and retinene$_1$ in the ratio of 2:1.

Several experiments of this type were performed with rhodopsin from cattle, frog and squid. In all cases the ratio of —SH to retinene$_1$ was about 2, the variation being from 1·8 to 2·4 and the mean, 2·1.

When these observations were made the stereoisometic aspects (see Chap. 5) of the formation and bleaching of rhodopsin were not yet appreciated, and an accurate value for the molecular extinction of rhodopsin was not available. In a subsequent paper, WALD and BROWN (1953) recalculated the results in the light of later knowledge, and obtained somewhat higher values for the mean values of the sulph-hydryl : retinene ratio, viz. 2·2 for cattle (mean of 6), 2·7 for frog (mean of 5) and 2·9 for squid (1 result).

STRUCTURE OF RHODOPSIN

As a result of these experiments WALD and BROWN (1952) suggested possible formulae for rhodopsin. They considered that —SH groups may take part in rhodopsin synthesis in two ways. 'They could be engaged directly in binding the prosthetic group to opsin; or alternatively they could yield hydrogen atoms for some reductive transformation of retinene$_1$ into the prosthetic group, simultaneously forming a disulphide (—S—S—) linkage. One could imagine also a combination of both types of reaction.'

The simplest reaction between retinene$_1$ and the —SH group of opsin is

$$C_{19}H_{27}C\overset{H}{\underset{O}{\diagup}} + HS\text{—opsin} \longrightarrow C_{19}H_{27}C\overset{H}{\underset{OH}{-}}\overset{\displaystyle H}{\underset{\displaystyle }{S}}\text{—opsin}$$

i.e. the formation of a hemi-thioacetal. If two —SH groups are involved, the following reaction is possible,

$$C_{19}H_{27}C\overset{H}{\underset{O}{\diagup}} + \overset{HS}{\underset{HS}{\diagdown\diagup}}\text{opsin} \longrightarrow C_{19}H_{27}C(H)\overset{S}{\underset{S}{\diagdown\diagup}}\text{opsin} + H_2O$$

As WALD and BROWN were aware, however, something more than this is required to yield rhodopsin. The reactions given above 'involve, without any compensatory change, the loss of the conjugated carbonyl group of retinene$_1$,' and so would yield products whose spectra would probably be displaced to shorter wavelengths, i.e. in the opposite direction to the observed shift which accompanies rhodopsin synthesis. Moreover, the higher values for the sulph-hydryl:retinene ratio obtained in the amended calculations pose a difficulty. WALD and BROWN (1953) therefore suggested that some sulph-hydryl may have had a different origin, i.e. that the bleaching of rhodopsin might be a denaturation process, resulting in the exposure of 'sulfhydryl and other groups on the protein, which had previously been unavailable to reagents.'

CONCLUSION

The work of the Liverpool school indicates that the first stable product formed when rhodopsin bleaches is indicator yellow, and that in this substance a carbon-nitrogen bond links retinene to protein. The work of the Harvard school, on the other hand, suggests that, in rhodopsin, retinene is coupled to protein via a sulphide or disulphide linkage.

In a recent paper, COLLINS, GREEN and MORTON (1954) have endeavoured to reach a compromise. Since the evidence from the syntheses (WALD and BROWN) suggests that rhodopsin is 'retinene—S—opsin' while the analytic evidence (MORTON and colleagues) indicates that it is 'retinene—N—opsin,' COLLINS, GREEN and MORTON have proposed that freshly formed 'retinene—S—opsin' undergoes an intra-molecular rearrangement to 'retinene—N—opsin.' In their view the N-compound, since it would absorb at longer wave-lengths than the S-compound, represents a more likely formulation for rhodopsin.

But this proposal allows that WALD and BROWN have provided adequate evidence for the involvement of the *aldehydic* group of retinene in the reaction with the sulph-hydryl groups of opsin. How-ever, for reasons to be given shortly, the writer believes that this is not the case and that, in consequence, the results of the two schools are not mutually exclusive, as might at first sight appear.

ASSESSMENT OF THE EVIDENCE

The work of MORTON and his colleagues leaves little room for doubting that indicator yellow is a key to the structure of rhodopsin.

It also seems to be firmly established that indicator yellow is retinene bound to protein through a nitrogen atom. The only evidence which might appear to contradict this conclusion is WALD and BROWN's observation (p. 117) that the synthesis of rhodopsin is most readily accomplished at pH 6, a hydrogen ion concentration at which retinene will readily condense with sulph-hydryl-, but not with amino-groups. But the syntheses were carried out with retinal extracts. In other words the solutions contained not only opsin and retinene but also other substances of retinal origin, some of which might act as catalysts. Thus the pH-activity curve (Fig. 4.5) may merely express the pH-activity of an enzyme: it can hardly be used as evidence against an aldehyde-amino condensation on the grounds that this reaction—when no catalyst is present—requires alkaline conditions.

On the other hand, the results of the amperometric titrations imply that sulph-hydryl groups as well are involved in the formation of rhodopsin from retinene and opsin. Since the aldehydic group of retinene is already bespoken for condensation with a protein amino-group, it seems likely that the protein sulph-hydryl groups must react with another part of the retinene molecule.

Taken as a whole, therefore, the evidence suggests that the chromophore of visual purple is bound to protein at a number of points. One bond is through a nitrogen atom, as in indicator yellow,

Indicator Yellow (see p. 109)

In addition the visual purple chromophore is held to the protein molecule by forces which involve the protein sulph-hydryl groups, and which are relaxed when visual purple 'bleaches' to indicator yellow. We have seen (p. 101) that the π-electrons of a conjugated polyene chain form orbitals extending over the whole length of the chain. We may suppose that, under certain conditions, viz. when the chromophore is of a suitable shape to fit the protein, the cloud of π-electrons overlaps, and consequently interacts with, the electrons of the opposing parts of the protein molecule to form new orbitals.

122

According to these ideas, the 'formula' for visual purple may be written,

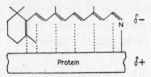

in which the vertical dotted lines represent the π-electron bonding between the polyene chain and protein and $\delta+$ and $\delta-$ the electrical tension which, because of electron displacements, is set up between them. This structure has a formal resemblance to that proposed by KUHN and SÖRENSEN (see KARRER and JUCKER, 1950) for ovoverdin, the blue-green chromoprotein of lobster shell.

Ovoverdin (chromophore attached at both
ends to the same protein molecule)

Astaxanthene, the chromophore of ovoverdin has λ_{max} about 500 mμ while ovoverdin itself has an absorption band centred at 640 mμ (STERN and SALOMON, 1937). The spectral interval between the λ_{max} of visual purple (500 mμ) and of retinene, its chromophore (385 mμ), is similar.

As described in the next chapter, only those retinenes of certain *cis-trans* conformations will react with opsin (visual purple protein) to form photosensitive pigments. When bleached, however, these pigments yield an inactive all-*trans* isomer of retinene. Thus when the chromophore of visual purple absorbs a quantum of energy, the consequent raising of the electronic levels must cause an alteration to the shape of the chromophore so that it no longer has the 'lock and key' correspondence to protein. The effect of this is twofold: the electric tension between chromophore and protein disappears (giving rise, perhaps, to excitation processes in the retinal rod) and the parts of the protein molecule which were 'covered' by the chromophore are now revealed (sulph-hydryl groups).

123

The existence of transient compounds (lumi- and meta-rhodopsin) between visual purple and indicator yellow suggests that the disengagement from the protein of the chromophore (as its conformation changes from a particular *cis-trans* isomer to the all-*trans* form of indicator yellow) takes place in stages.

REFERENCES

BALL, S., COLLINS, F. D., DALVI, P. D. and MORTON, R. A. (1949). Studies in vitamin A. 11: Reactions of retinene$_1$ with amino compounds. *Biochem. J.*, **45**, 304–307.

BALL, S., COLLINS, F. D. and MORTON, R. A. (1948). Indicator yellow and retinene$_1$. *Nature, Lond.*, **162**, 222.

BALL, S., COLLINS, F. D., MORTON, R. A. and STUBBS. A. L. (1948). Chemistry of visual processes. *Nature, Lond.*, **161**, 424–426.

BALL, S., GOODWIN, T. W. and MORTON, R. A. (1948). Studies on vitamin A. 5: The preparation of retinene$_1$—vitamin A aldehyde. *Biochem. J.*, **42**, 516–523.

BLISS, A. F. (1948). Retinene$_1$ and indicator yellow. *Nature, Lond.*, **162**, 661–662.

COLLINS, F. D. (1953). Rhodopsin and indicator yellow. *Nature, Lond.*, **171**, 469–471.

COLLINS, F. D., GREEN, J. N. and MORTON, R. A. (1954). Studies in rhodopsin. 7: Regeneration of rhodopsin by comminuted ox retina. *Biochem. J.*, **56**, 493–498.

COLLINS, F. D., LOVE, R. M. and MORTON, R. A. (1952). Studies in rhodopsin. 4: Preparation of rhodopsin. *Biochem. J.*, **51**, 292–298.

COLLINS, F. D. and MORTON, R. A. (1950a). Studies on rhodopsin. 1: Methods of extraction and the absorption spectrum. *Biochem. J.*, **47**, 3–10.

COLLINS, F. D. and MORTON, R. A. (1950b). Studies on rhodopsin. 2: Indicator yellow. *Biochem. J.*, **47**, 10–17.

COLLINS, F. D. and MORTON, R. A. (1950c). Studies in rhodopsin. 3: Rhodopsin and transient orange. *Biochem. J.*, **47**, 18–24.

CHASE, A. M. (1936). Anomalies in the absorption spectrum and bleaching kinetics of visual purple. *J. gen. Physiol.*, **19**, 577–599.

CRESCITELLI, F. and DARTNALL, H. J. A. (1953). Human visual purple. *Nature, Lond.*, **172**, 195–197.

DARTNALL, H. J. A. (1948). Indicator yellow and retinene$_1$, *Nature, London.*, **162**, 222.

HAWKINS, E. G. E. and HUNTER, R. F. (1944). Vitamin A aldehyde (Axerophthal). *J. chem. Soc.*, 411.

HECHT, S. (1942). The chemistry of visual substances. *Ann. Rev. Biochem.*, **11**, 465–496.

HUBBARD, R. (1954). The molecular weight of rhodopsin and the nature of the rhodopsin-digitonin complex. *J. gen. Physiol.*, **37**, 381–399.

KARRER, P. and JUCKER, E. (1950). *Carotenoids.* Elsevier Publishing Co. Inc., Amsterdam.

LEVY, M. and SILBERMAN, D. E. (1937). The reactions of amino and imino acids with formaldehyde. *J. biol. Chem.,* **118,** 723–734.

LYTHGOE, R. J. (1937). The absorption spectra of visual purple and of indicator yellow. *J. Physiol.,* **89,** 331–358.

MORTON, R. A. (1944). Chemical aspects of the visual process. *Nature, Lond.,* **153,** 69–71.

MORTON, R. A. and GOODWIN, T. W. (1944). Preparation of retinene *in vitro. Nature, Lond.,* **153,** 405–406.

STERN, K. G. and SALOMON, K. (1937). On ovoverdin, the carotenoid-protein pigment of the egg of the lobster. *J. biol. Chem.,* **122,** 461–475.

WALD, G. (1938). On rhodopsin in solution. *J. gen. Physiol.,* **21,** 795–832.

WALD, G, (1949). The photochemistry of vision. *Documenta Ophthal.,* **3,** 94–13.

WALD, G. and BROWN, P. K. (1950). The synthesis of rhodopsin from retinene$_1$. *Proc. nat. Acad. Sci. Wash.,* **36,** 84–92.

WALD, G. and BROWN, P. K. (1952). The role of sulfhydryl groups in the bleaching and synthesis of rhodopsin. *J. gen. Physiol.,* **35,** 797–821.

WALD, G. and BROWN, P. K. (1953). The molar extinction of rhodopsin. *J. gen. Physiol.,* **37,** 189–200.

WALD, G. and HUBBARD, R. (1949). The reduction of retinene to vitamin A$_2$ *in vitro. J. gen. Physiol.,* **32,** 367–389.

CHAPTER FIVE

Isomerism and the Visual Pigments

In 1951 HUBBARD and WALD found that rhodopsin (visual purple) could be synthesized by placing in darkness a solution containing four components. The four components were opsin—the protein moiety of the rhodopsin molecule, vitamin A_1—the precursor of the chromophore, and liver alcohol dehydrogenase and cozymase—the enzyme and coenzyme, respectively, which oxidize vitamin A_1 to retinene$_1$.

The synthesis was originally carried out using a fish liver oil concentrate as the source of vitamin A_1. When, later, an attempt was made to repeat the experiment with crystalline vitamin A_1, hardly any rhodopsin was formed.

The difference in behaviour between the two samples of vitamin A_1 suggested to HUBBARD and WALD that a particular *form* of vitamin A_1 was required for the synthesis. Liver oils are known to contain a mixture of different varieties or isomers of vitamin A_1—all of which have the same formula and differ only in respect of their spatial conformation. Crystalline vitamin A_1, on the other hand is a single isomer and one which, as the experiment showed, is unsuitable for the synthesis.

These important observations by WALD and his collaborators, though recent, have already led to a considerable extension of our knowledge of the visual pigments. In order to appreciate the results obtained it is necessary first to consider some aspects of isomerism.

CIS-TRANS ISOMERISM

When two atoms are united by a single covalent bond, either atom is capable of independent rotation about the bond. When, however, they are linked by a *double* covalent bond, the mutual aspect of the atoms—and hence of any other groups which are attached to them— is fixed. In other words free rotation about a double bond cannot occur. In such cases, if the doubly-bound atoms are also connected to *dissimilar* atoms or groups, the whole molecule can exist in different non-labile forms.

An example of isomerism arising from these causes is that of maleic and fumaric acids,

maleic acid   fumaric acid

In maleic acid the two carboxyl groups lie on the same side of the molecule; in fumaric acid, on opposite sides. The two isomers differ from each other in both physical and chemical properties. Thus, because the carboxyl groups in maleic acid are adjacent, the elements of water can be readily stripped from the molecule, e.g. by heating, with the formation of a stable anhydride. But no anhydride of fumaric acid is known.

The type of isomerism typified by maleic and fumaric acid is known as *cis-trans* isomerism. Compounds in which similar groups are on the same side of the molecule are called *cis* forms; those in which they are on opposite sides being called *trans* forms.

cis isomer   *trans* isomer

Although the most familiar examples of *cis-trans* isomers involve orientation about a double bond, *cis-trans* isomerism can also occur about a single bond, provided free rotation about that bond is prevented—as, for example, when the atoms form part of a rigid ring structure.

CIS-TRANS ISOMERISM IN COMPOUNDS CONTAINING MORE THAN ONE DOUBLE BOND

When the molecule contains more than one double bond—for example, in substances such as the vitamins A, the retinenes and the diphenylpolyenes—*cis-trans* isomerism may give rise to a multiplicity of isomers. Free rotation about the single bonds is, of course, still possible and formula for the hexatrienes such as

can be regarded as equivalent, for the lability of transition from one form to another precludes the possibility of obtaining a separate specimen of any one. By contrast, since rotation about a double bond is not allowed, several non-labile, and hence separable *cis-trans* isomers, are possible. Conventional formula for these—eight in the present instance—are given below.

Theoretically possible *cis-trans* isomers of the hexatrienes
$$R—(CH=CH)_3—R'$$

Theoretically, a polyene of the formula $R—(CH=CH)_n—R'$, containing n double bonds, can exist in 2^n different *cis-trans* conformations. When the molecule is symmetrical, i.e. when R is the same as R', the number of isomers is less, namely $2^{n-1} + 2^{p-1}$ where $p = n/2$ if n is even and $(n + 1)/2$ if n is odd.

STERIC HINDRANCE

However, some theoretically possible forms involve the folding-back of the molecule upon itself to such an extent as to cause mutual obstruction by different parts. Obstruction is more likely in highly branched molecules; for example, when one or more of the hydrogens in the ethylenic groups —CH=CH— are replaced by bulkier groups such as methyl (—CH$_3$).

The mutual interference between different parts of the same molecule is called steric hindrance. It complicates the theory of isomerism. Sometimes steric hindrance, through preventing free rotation about a single bond, 'locks' what would normally be interchangeable forms into non-labile isomers. For example, terphenyl derivatives which are substituted in positions *ortho* to the pivot bonds joining the phenyl groups and which are unsymmetrically substituted in the terminal phenyl groups can exist in *cis-trans* forms (STANLEY and ADAMS, 1929).

cis   *trans*

Independent rotation about the pivot bonds is, in these cases, prevented by the steric hindrance of the A and X, and A and Y groups.

In other molecules steric hindrance may result in a reduction of the number of *cis-trans* isomers. As an example we may consider vitamin A$_1$, which has two methyl groups attached to the conjugated chain.

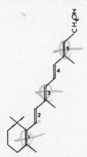

Since vitamin A$_1$ possesses four ethylenic groups (the double bonds of which are marked 2, 3, 4 and 5 in the formula above) 2^4, that is, sixteen *cis-trans* forms are theoretically possible. Not all these forms are realizable, however.

In a complex molecule like this, the effects of steric hindrance can be more readily appreciated with the aid of models in which the spatial orientation of valency bonds and the sizes and distances apart of the constituent atoms are all properly represented.

According to PAULING (1939) a *cis* conformation in the carotenoids and related substances can be assumed only by those double bonds which carry methyl side chains (i.e. bonds 3 and 5) and not by those which are adjacent to a C—CH$_3$ group (bonds 2 and 4) or which are located in a ring (bond 1).

(a)   (b)

Cis-conformations for (a) =CH—C(CH$_3$)=CH—CH= and
(b) =C(CH$_3$)—CH=CH—CH=

In (a) which is representative of bonds 3 and 5 there is little overlapping between the spheres of influence of the hydrogen atoms and the strain thus caused can in any case be alleviated by small rotations (about the single carbon-carbon bonds) out of coplanarity. In (b), representing bonds 2 and 4 the overlap between the hydrogen and the bulkier methyl group is much greater and cannot be relieved by rotation about single bonds. The *cis* form in this example is a strained and hence unstable configuration.

Because of these limitations only four (2^2), instead of sixteen (2^4) isomers are likely for vitamin A$_1$. Conventional formulae for these are given below:

all *trans*   3-*cis*   5-*cis*   3,5 *di-cis*

Unhindered *cis-trans* isomers of vitamin A$_1$

130

DIFFERENCES BETWEEN *CIS* AND *TRANS* ISOMERS

The differences in properties between *cis* and *trans* isomers are best illustrated with reference to the carotenoids. These substances, containing 40 carbon atoms per molecule can be considered to be built up from eight isoprene $(CH_2=CH—C(CH_3)=CH_2)$ units. The main structural characteristic of the carotenoids is a reversal of direction of the C_5 (isoprene) units at the centre of the molecule—'as if four C_5 units had combined head to tail to form a C_{20} unit, two of which then combined tail to tail to give a C_{40} carotenoid' (GOODWIN, 1953).

The skeletal basis of the carotenoid (C_{40}) molecule in terms of 'isoprene (C_5) units'

The following remarks, though applying specifically to the carotenoids are also applicable to the closely related 'half carotenoids,' i.e. C_{20} units, such as the retinenes and the vitamins A and also to polyenes in general.

The all-*trans* configuration for a carotenoid molecule is one which involves least strain. Therefore, it is not surprising that, with a few exceptions, the natural carotenoids possess entirely *trans* configurations. By suitable procedures (described in the next section) the naturally occurring all-*trans* carotenoids can be converted into a mixture of isomers and these can be separated by chromatographic analysis. In all cases it is found that the mixtures obtained by isomerization exhibit certain common features with respect to the original all-*trans* forms:

1. They are more soluble.
2. Their melting points are lower.
3. They absorb at shorter wavelengths $(3–4 \, m\mu)$ in the visible region than the parent all-*trans* isomer.
4. Their extinction coefficients (intensities of absorption) are lower.
5. They are often characterized by the development of a new absorption band in the near ultraviolet. These new bands are called '*cis*-peaks.'

131

6. There are often large changes in optical rotatory power (if the molecule contains one or more asymmetric carbon atoms).

Some of these effects are illustrated for the case of β-carotene in Fig. 5.1. The reduction in intensity of the absorption band in the

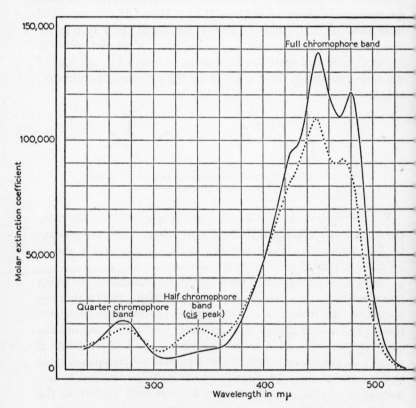

FIG. 5.1. Light-absorbing characteristics of β-carotene, a typical C_{40} carotenoid, and the effect of molecular shape (isomeric form). —— trans-β-carotene, ... cis-β-carotene.

visible spectrum and the appearance of the *cis* peak in the near ultraviolet (340 mμ) on isomerization are well shown. In most C_{40} carotenoids (in hexane solution) the centre of the *cis* peak lies at 142 ± 2 mμ from the longwave maximum.

Interpretation of absorption spectra. As exemplified in Fig. 5.1 for β-carotene, the carotenoids absorb light in three spectral regions, viz.: (1) in the visible (400–500 mμ), where the most intense absorption band is located, (2) in the near ultraviolet (c. 340 mμ), the region of 'cis peaks' and (3) in the far ultraviolet (c. 280 mμ).

These absorption characteristics can be interpreted in terms of molecular structure (LEWIS and CALVIN, 1939; PAULING, 1939, ZECHMEISTER, 1944). The chain of alternate single and double valency bonds,

$$\text{〰〰〰〰} \tag{1}$$

can resonate between a large number of ionic forms such as:

$$\tag{2}$$

The conventional formula (1) represents the condition of a normal, unexcited molecule: the formulae (2), a few of the possible resonance structures for an excited one. Because of the multiplicity of ionic forms, however, no single form is adequate to describe an excited molecule. As described in Chapter 4 (p. 101), the electrons which are 'left over,' after allocating a single covalent bond throughout the conjugated chain, mutually interact to form so-called π-orbitals.

The oscillating electric vector of light causes the π-electrons to congregate backwards and forwards along the conjugated chain, first at one end and then at the other. When the light is of the proper frequency to correspond with the rhythm of these oscillations it is strongly absorbed (the fundamental band in the visible). The intensity of the band is proportional to the square of the regularly alternating dipole moment of the molecule, and hence to the square of the length of the conjugated chain.

The first overtone band in the near ultraviolet (cis-peak at c. 340 mμ) arises from an oscillation of π-electrons towards the middle of the conjugated chain and from the middle towards the two ends. The dipoles of these two half oscillations are opposed and hence the absorption band is of very low intensity in 'straight' or all-trans isomers. In a cis isomer, however, the molecule is bent and hence

133

has a resultant dipole at right angles to the chain which gives rise to the *cis* peak or 'half chromophore' band.

The second overtone band in the far ultraviolet (*c.* 280 mμ) results from an induced concentration of π-electrons alternately in the first and third and in the second and fourth quarters of the chain. These quarter oscillations confer an overall dipole moment on the molecule and one which is maximal for an all-*trans* isomer and less for any *cis*-form.

A *cis* bond has its greatest effect when situated at the centre of the chain for then it reduces the total chromophore length by a factor, of cos 30° and hence decreases the intensity of the visible or full chromophore band by cos² 30 = 0·75. The *cis*-peak or half-chromophore band on the other hand is then maximal.

This discussion can be summarized in tabular form as follows:

Absorption characteristics of the polyenes

Band	Spectral* location	Intensity of absorption in all-trans isomers	Intensity of absorption after isomerization
Full chromophore	Visible	Very great	Decreased (maximum decrease 25%)
Half chromophore	Near ultraviolet	Very small	Increased to moderate intensity
Quarter chromophore	Far ultraviolet	Moderate	Decreased

* These spectral locations refer to polyenes containing about 12 conjugated double bonds in the chain.

INTERCONVERSION OF *CIS-TRANS* ISOMERS

Isomerization, that is the conversion of a specimen of a given configuration into a mixture of other *cis-trans* forms, can be effected in a number of ways: for example, by reflux distillation of a solution of the carotenoid, by melting the crystals, by treatment with iodine or acids, and also by illumination. Separation of the mixture of isomers can then be carried out on the chromatograph column, for the strength of adsorption of the isomers varies considerably.

What is the mechanism of isomerization? A conjugated chain is potentially capable of interchanging its double and single bonds. This event, followed by a return to the original state could result in the formation of a different isomer if, between the interchange and the reinstatement, rotations about single bonds take place. For example:

all-*trans* form

a *cis*-isomer

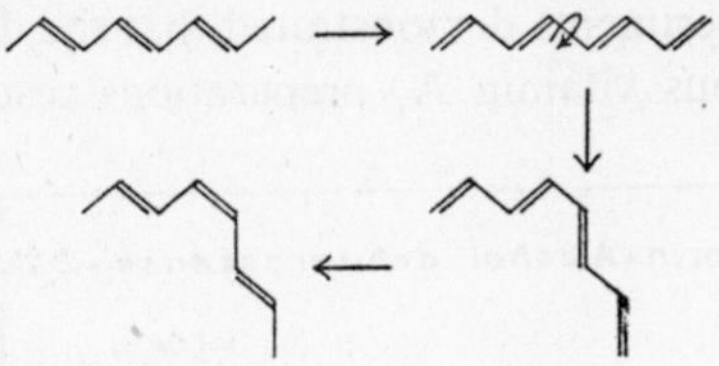

Any process which facilitates a reversible interchange of single and double bonds in a conjugated chain will cause isomerization to occur. Such changes might be initiated by the accession of energy to the molecule, either from collision with other molecules (resulting in thermal isomerization) or by absorption of light.

The effect of iodine in facilitating isomerization might result from photosensitization of the carotenoid to visible light, which iodine strongly absorbs, or from an ephemeral addition of iodine across a double bond, thereby converting it temporarily to a single bond.

CIS-TRANS ISOMERS OF VITAMIN A_1 IN THE SYNTHESIS OF VISUAL PURPLE

The present chapter was opened with WALD and HUBBARD'S observation that rhodopsin can be synthesized in solution from liver oil vitamin A_1 but not from crystalline vitamin A_1.

The results of the experiment are shown in Fig. 5.2. The synthesis was followed by measuring the rising extinction at 500 mμ with time (Fig. 5.2, left). In the case of the solution containing the liver oil concentrate (empty circles) the rise was very marked and was still proceeding after 3 hr. With the solution containing crystalline all-*trans* vitamin A_1 (filled circles), however, there was only a moderate rise in extinction which ceased after about 1 hr. After 3 hr hydroxylamine was added to both solutions to break up 'fortuitous combinations of retinene with other complexes.' The changes in absorption caused by bleaching (difference spectra) were then measured and are shown on the right of Fig. 5.2. Crystalline vitamin A_1 had yielded only about one tenth as much rhodopsin as had that from the liver oil concentrate. Another isomer of vitamin A_1, namely crystalline *neo*-vitamin A_1a (ROBESON and BAXTER, 1947) was found to be

135

ineffective also. However, both the all-*trans* and *neo-a* isomers could be made as effective as the liver oil concentrate by exposing them to light in the presence of iodine (see Fig. 5.3).

These experiments demonstrated that the differences in behaviour of the various vitamin A_1 preparations resulted from geometrical

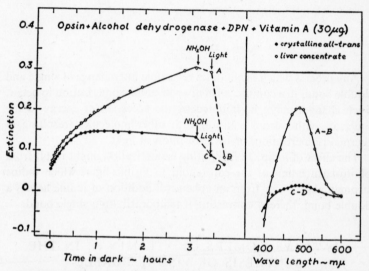

FIG. 5.2. Synthesis of rhodopsin (visual purple) from all-*trans* vitamin A_1 and from the vitamin A of fish liver oil. Cattle opsin, horse liver alcohol dehydrogenase and cozymase (DPN) were incubated in darkness with the vitamins A. Curves on the left show the rising extinction at 500 mμ as the synthesis proceeded. Hydroxylamine (NH$_2$OH) was then added to destroy spurious retinene complexes. The synthesized pigments were then bleached by light (*A* to *B*, *C* to *D*). Difference spectra for the bleachings are shown on the right.

(*Hubbard and Wald*, 1952)

isomerism and indicated that the synthesis of rhodopsin requires a specific form of vitamin A_1 and one which is neither the all-*trans* nor the *neo-a* isomer.

The site of isomer specificity. In the synthesis of rhodopsin from vitamin A_1, two proteins are involved. The first of these is the enzyme protein, alcohol dehydrogenase which catalyses the oxidation of vitamin A_1 to retinene$_1$; the second is opsin, the protein of rhodopsin with which retinene combines. Either or both of these proteins could require a specific isomer; the first, of vitamin A_1 and the second, of retinene₁. However, HUBBARD and WALD found that all-*trans* vitamin A_1 and liver vitamin A were both readily oxidized to retinene by alcohol dehydrogenase and cozymase, in fact the all-*trans* isomer (inactive in the synthesis of rhodopsin) was the more reactive.

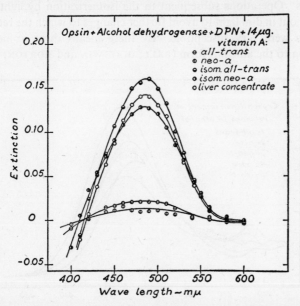

FIG. 5.3. Synthesis of rhodopsin from vitamin A_1 of five different types. Curves show the difference spectra obtained on bleaching the pigments synthesized from equal amounts of each form of vitamin A_1.
(*Hubbard and Wald*, 1952)

This experiment strongly suggests that it is in the combination of opsin with retinene that a particular stereoisomer is essential.

ISOMERS OF RETINENE₁

Opsin and retinene₁ will react directly to form rhodopsin without the intervention of the coenzyme and enzyme necessary when vitamin A_1 is the starting material. For this reason, and also because it is an easier matter to prepare and separate pure specimens of the stereoisomers of retinene₁, than of vitamin A_1, the problem of determining the stereo-requirements of opsin was undertaken by HUBBARD, GREGERMAN and WALD using retinene₁ instead of vitamin A_1.

All-*trans* retinene₁ and *neo*-retinene₁ *a* were prepared from all-*trans* vitamin A₁ and *neo*-vitamin A₁*a* by oxidation with manganese dioxide. Other stereoisomers of retinene₁ were obtained by irradiating a solution of all-*trans* retinene₁ and then chromatographing the mixture of isomers. Operations subsequent to the isomerization by light were carried out in dim light to avoid further changes to which the retinene isomers were very susceptible. By these means three isomers in addition to the all-*trans* form (BALL, GOODWIN and MORTON, 1948)

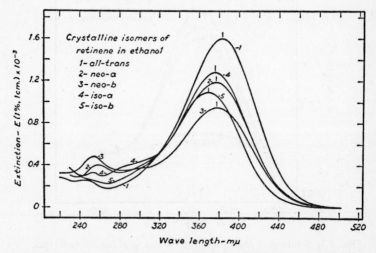

FIG. 5.4. Density spectra (in ethyl alcohol) of five retinene₁ isomers.
(*Hubbard, Gregerman and Wald*, 1953)

and *neo*-retinene₁ *a* (DALVI and MORTON, 1952) were prepared. These were called *neo*-retinene₁ *b*, isolated by HUBBARD, GREGERMAN and WALD (1953) and *iso*-retinenes₁ *a* and *b* isolated by the Organic Research Laboratory of Distillation Products Industries (see HUBBARD and WALD, 1952; HUBBARD, GREGERMAN and WALD, 1953). The melting points and absorption characteristics of these isomers, some of which were obtained crystalline, are shown in the following table. The full absorption spectra in ethyl alcohol of the five isomers are shown in Fig. 5.4.

HUBBARD, GREGERMAN and WALD (op. cit.) found that all five isomers gave a blue colour when mixed with antimony trichloride in chloroform. The absorption spectra of the blue solutions were identical in each case ($\lambda_{max} = 660$ mμ, E_{max} (1 per cent, 1 cm) =

Melting points and absorption characteristics of retinene$_1$ isomers in various solvents

(from Hubbard, Gregerman and Wald, 1953, Wald and Brown, 1953)

Isomer	Melting point	Solvent							
		Petroleum ether		Ethyl alcohol		Chloroform		1% aqueous digitonin	
		λ_{max} (mμ)	E^*	λ_{max} (mμ)	E^*	λ_{max} (mμ)	E^*	λ_{max} (mμ)	E^*
All-*trans*	61–62°	369	1720	383	1510	390	1520	389	1350
Neo-retinene *a*	75°	364	1290	377	1190	385	1190	381	—
Neo-retinene *b*	—	363	—	377·5	(900–1000)	386	—	384	(825)
Iso-retinene *a*	64·5°	362·5	1360	376	1270	384	1265	382	—
Iso-retinene *b*	—	—	—	369	1090	378·5	—	375	—

* For 1 per cent solution in a cell of 1 cm path length. The molecular extinction coefficient is obtained by multiplying by $\dfrac{\text{M.W.}}{10}$, i.e. by 28·4.

3,780). This reaction thus affords a convenient means of estimating retinene without regard for its stereochemical form.

ALLOCATION OF STRUCTURES TO THE RETINENE$_1$ ISOMERS

In attempting to assign spatial formulae to the five retinenes$_1$ we are faced with an immediate difficulty: only four isomers are expected according to the simple theory of *cis-trans* isomerism, outlined in the earlier part of this chapter. The fact that five isomers have been described means, either that the simple theory is incorrect, or, that some of the isomers depend on other than *cis-trans* differences. Although, at present, it is not possible to reach an unequivocal solution of this problem, it is interesting to examine the evidence.

The arguments by which spatial formulae for the isomers can be deduced depend very largely on comparisons between absorption spectra (see Fig. 5.4). Since the retinenes are 'half-carotenoids' their principal absorption bands lie in the near ultraviolet, roughly in the '*cis* peak' region for 'whole' carotenoids (e.g. β-carotene, Fig. 5.1): likewise, the '*cis* peak' region of the retinenes is located in the far ultraviolet; in roughly the same spectral region as the quarter chromophore bands of 'whole' carotenoids. Apart from these differences from true carotenoids—differences which, of course, arise from the shorter conjugated chain—the retinenes have absorption spectra which are analogous to those of the carotenoids and the same rules apply.

Considering first the principal bands of the retinenes we see (Fig. 5.4) that the all-*trans* isomer has its maximum (in alcohol) at 383 mμ, while three other isomers have their maxima about 6 mμ lower, viz. *iso-a* at 376 mμ, *neo-a* at 377 mμ and *neo-b* at 377·5 mμ. Such a shift of maximum corresponds—in carotenoids—to a single *cis* linkage in the conjugated chain. The remaining isomer, *iso*-retinene *b*, has a principal-band maximum at 369 mμ, 14 mμ lower than that for the all-*trans* isomer, and thus indicating the presence of two *cis* links. From a comparison between the principal bands therefore, it would seem that the five isomers include an all-*trans* form, three mono-*cis* forms, and one di-*cis* form.

How does this conclusion tally with the absorption characteristics in the *cis* peak region? The all-*trans* isomer has low and poorly defined absorption here (Fig. 5.4), as would be expected, but so also have *iso*-retinenes$_1$ *a* and *b*, the presumptive mono- and di-*cis* isomers. Only the *neo*-retinenes$_1$ *a* and *b*, show the well defined *cis* peaks expected of mono-*cis* isomers. In any case, if there are three mono-*cis* isomers (*iso-a*, *neo-a* and *neo-b*) one of them must be a sterically hindered form, viz. the 2- or 4-*cis* isomer.

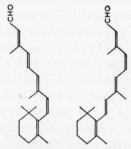

2-*cis*-retinene$_1$ 4-*cis*-retinene$_1$

Now recent work with the polyenes (OROSHNIK *et al.*, 1952, GARBERS *et al.*, 1952) has indeed shown that compounds containing sterically hindered *cis* linkages can be prepared. But the absorption spectra of such compounds are much altered (low intensities of absorption and λ_{max} displaced 20–40 mμ). None of the presumably mono-*cis* isomers of retinene$_1$ show such degradation of absorption.

The *iso*-retinenes$_1$ *a* and *b* show certain peculiarities in their absorption spectra in comparison with the remaining retinenes. Below 240 mμ (Fig. 5.4) their absorption curves rise to cross the other spectra while *iso*-retinene$_1$ *a* has a unique plateau of absorption in the range 280–320 mμ. HUBBARD, GREGERMAN and WALD (1953) also observed that the behaviour of the *iso*-retinenes on subjecting them to isomerizing treatments set them apart from the others. Thus while *iso*-retinene$_1$ *b* readily isomerizes to *iso*-retinene$_1$ *a* the conversion of *iso*-retinene$_1$ *a* to the remaining retinenes is difficult.

In line with these differences, WOODWARD (cited by HUBBARD, GREGERMAN and WALD, 1953) suggested that one or more of the retinenes might have an α-ionone rather than a β-ionone ring structure:

α-ionone   β-ionone

The change from a β-ionone to an α-ionone ring results in much the same sort of λ_{max} displacement as would the introduction of a *cis*-link. According to this idea, the two *iso*-retinenes are to be regarded as α-retinenes and the three other retinenes as β-retinenes as follows:

all trans *retinene*$_1$ neo-*retinene*$_1$ *a*   neo-*retinene*$_1$ *b*
$\lambda_{max} = 383$ mμ $\lambda_{max} = 377$ mμ $\lambda_{max} = 377 \cdot 5$ mμ
(all *trans*, β-retinene)   (5 *cis*, β-retinene)   (3 *cis*, β-retinene)

141

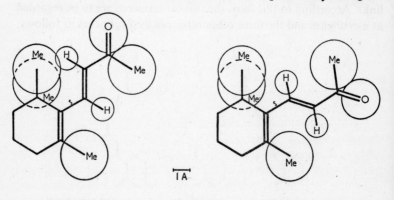

iso-*retinene*₁ *a*
$\lambda_{max} = 376$ mμ
(all *trans*, α-retinene)

iso-*retinene*₁ *b*
$\lambda_{max} = 369$ mμ
(5 *cis* or 3 *cis*, α-retinene)

Possible structures for the five known isomers of retinene₁. The λ_{max}
are for alcohol solutions.

(*Hubbard, Gregerman and Wald*, 1953)

As indicated above *neo*-retinene₁ *b* is written as the symmetrical
3-*cis* isomer because it has the more intense *cis* peak and the less
intense main band (see Fig. 5.4 and compare p. 134)—leaving *neo*-
retinene₁ *a* as the 5-*cis* isomer (ROBESON and BAXTER, 1947).

According to these ideas 3,5 di-*cis*, β-retinene₁, another mono-*cis*,
α-retinene₁ and 3,5 di-*cis*, α-retinene₁ remain to be discovered.

It is not easy to assess the likelihood of an α-retinene structure for
the *iso*-retinenes. The conversion of β- into α-carotene (which differ
in the same sense as α- and β-retinenes) requires very energetic

s-*trans*

s-*cis*

FIG. 5.5. s-*trans* and s-*cis* forms of β-ionone.

142

chemical treatment. On these grounds it would seem unlikely that β-retinenes could pass into α-retinenes merely as the result of isomerization by light.

Yet another possibility, which so far has not been considered, is worth examining. The configuration of β-ionone itself has been the subject of some speculation (BRAUDE *et al.*, 1949, HENBEST and WOODS, 1952). β-ionone can exist in two stereoisomeric forms. The spatial configuration of these is shown in Fig. 5.5, the large, medium and small circles representing, respectively, the spheres of influence of methyl, oxygen and hydrogen groups. Steric hindrance between the hydrogen atom and the *gem* dimethyl group interferes with rotation about the single bond marked s in Fig. 5.5, with the result that *s-trans* and *s-cis* forms of β-ionone are possible (see p. 129). Assuming that a similar situation occurs in the retinene molecule, the exceptional properties of the *iso*-retinenes could be explained by supposing that they are *s-cis* forms of β-retinene rather than that they are hypothetical α-retinenes.

iso-retinene$_1$ a
$\lambda_{max} = 376$ mμ
(*s-cis*, β-retinene)

iso-retinene$_1$ b
$\lambda_{max} = 369$ mμ
(*s-cis*, 5-*cis*, or *s-cis*, 3-*cis*-β-retinene)

Alternative possible structure for the *iso*-retinenes$_1$ (compare p. 142).

It is doubtful, however, whether all the complexities possible with the retinene$_1$ molecule are yet known. The steric possibilities of even the *cyclo*hexane ring are still under discussion (see, for example, KLYNE, 1954). The structures of the five known isomers of retinene$_1$ must, therefore, remain uncertain for the present. It is possible that further isomers will be discovered and these may help to unravel the problem.

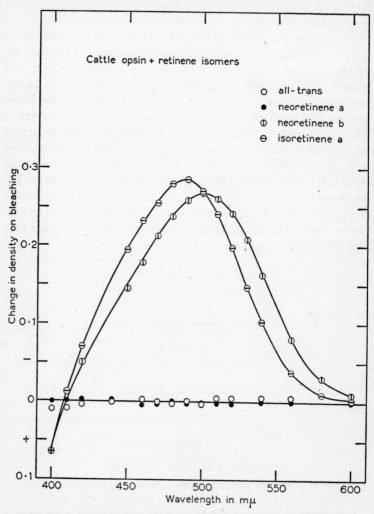

FIG. 5.6. Difference spectra of the products formed by the reaction of various retinene₁ isomers with cattle opsin. All-*trans* retinene₁ and *neo*-retinene₁ *a* yield no light-sensitive pigment; *neo*-retinene₁ *b* yields rhodopsin, and *iso*-retinene₁ *a* yields *iso*-rhodopsin.
(*After Hubbard and Wald, 1952*)

REACTION BETWEEN THE RETINENES$_1$ AND CATTLE OPSIN

HUBBARD and WALD (1952) studied the reaction in digitonin solution between the five isomers of retinene$_1$ and opsin (prepared from cattle retinae). The mixtures of opsin and each of the retinene$_1$ isomers (in excess) were allowed to stand in darkness for $1\frac{1}{2}$–$2\frac{3}{4}$ hr. After adding hydroxylamine to prevent further reaction, the difference spectrum of the product (if any) was then obtained by measuring the absorption spectra of the solutions before and after bleaching. The results obtained for the all-*trans*, *neo-a*, *neo-b* and *iso-a* isomers of retinene$_1$ are given in Fig. 5.6. This shows that the all-*trans* and *neo-a* isomers yielded no photosensitive pigment; the *neo-b* isomer produced a rhodopsin apparently identical with the naturally-occurring visual pigment; while *iso*-retinene$_1$ *a* yielded a photosensitive pigment having λ_{max} at about 487 mμ, about 13 mμ lower than that for the visual pigment. The remaining isomer, *iso*-retinene$_1$ *b* was found to be inactive, but, because it isomerized fairly readily even in darkness to form *iso*-retinene$_1$ *a*, some photosensitive pigment with λ_{max} at 487 mμ was obtained.

Thus of the five known isomers of retinene$_1$ only two (*neo-b* and *iso-a*) could be induced to react with cattle opsin to form photosensitive pigments. The pigment with $\lambda_{max} = 487$ mμ obtained from *iso*-retinene *a* was called *iso*-rhodopsin to distinguish it from the naturally-occurring pigment cattle rhodopsin obtained from *neo*-retinene$_1$ *b*.

The term *iso*-rhodopsin has also been used to describe regenerated rhodopsin. In this context (COLLINS and MORTON, 1950) it has $\lambda_{max} = 487$–488 when derived from rat or cattle rhodopsin and $\lambda_{max} = 493$ mμ when derived from frog rhodopsin.

Reaction kinetics. The reaction between opsin and *neo*-retinene$_1$ *b* the precursor of rhodopsin, follows the course of a bimolecular reaction (Fig. 5.7). This would be expected if the formation of rhodopsin involves a reaction between one molecule of opsin and one of retinene (cf. p. 94). CHASE and SMITH (1939), on the other hand, found that the small amount of pigment regenerated in bleached solutions of frog rhodopsin was formed according to the kinetics of a monomolecular reaction. HUBBARD and WALD (1952) reconciled this result with their own by pointing out that the bleaching of rhodopsin results mainly in the production of non-active isomers of retinene (thus accounting for the small degree of regeneration usually observed). In these circumstances, the opsin is present in large excess and the course of regeneration appears to be monomolecular, because the concentration of opsin is only slightly reduced through combina-

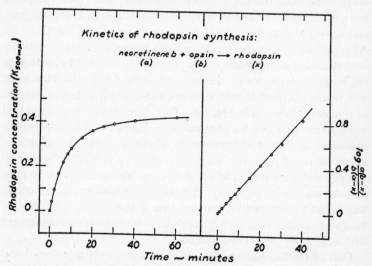

FIG. 5.7. The kinetics of the synthesis, in solution, of rhodopsin from *neo*-retinene$_1$ *b* and cattle opsin. Curve on left shows the rising extinction at 500 mμ as the synthesis proceeds. Straight line on right indicates that the reaction follows a bimolecular course.

(*Hubbard and Wald*, 1952)

tion with the active isomers present and is, therefore, effectively constant throughout the reaction.

THE STEREOCHEMICAL FORM OF RETINENE$_1$ IN BLEACHED RHODOPSIN SOLUTIONS

When a solution of rhodopsin is bleached at ordinary temperatures, and then placed in darkness there is normally very little regeneration of photosensitive pigment. This suggests that the retinene or retinene-protein (indicator yellow) formed by bleaching is not of the necessary spatial configuration required for synthesis.

CHASE (1937) and CHASE and SMITH (1939) found that when rhodopsin was bleached by light which included the short wavelength region of the spectrum there was some regeneration of pigment in darkness, but that if yellow light were used for bleaching there was

146

little or no regeneration. They found further, that if a solution bleached by yellow light was then exposed to blue, further changes (bleaching) occurred—maximal at short wavelengths—and that the solution would then exhibit some regeneration. They concluded that the solutions contained a yellow (i.e. short-wave-absorbing) substance the bleaching of which assisted in the regeneration of rhodopsin.

These observations were confirmed by HUBBARD and WALD (1952). Thus a solution of cattle rhodopsin which was bleached by orange light, regenerated in darkness to the extent of 7 per cent; another sample of the same preparation, when bleached with white light, regenerated 26 per cent. When the regenerated pigments were bleached a second time—but with the bleaching lights reversed—there was a similar difference between the amounts of pigment subsequently regenerated, viz. 8 per cent in one case (where orange light was used for the second bleaching) and 26 per cent in the other.

These results were explained by HUBBARD and WALD in terms of the isomerization of the retinene released as a result of bleaching. The absorption spectra of rhodopsin solutions after bleaching were slightly different depending on whether a non-isomerizing (long wavelength) or isomerizing (short wavelength) light had been used for bleaching. Thus when a solution of rhodopsin (pH 6·5) was bleached by orange light the product of bleaching had $\lambda_{max} =$ 386 mμ. On irradiating the bleached solution with white light the maximum shifted to 380 mμ. When digitonin solutions of all-*trans* neo-a and neo-b retinenes$_1$ were isomerized by exposure to white light a similar shift occurred only in the case of all-*trans* retinene$_1$. HUBBARD and WALD thus concluded that when rhodopsin was bleached by non-isomerizing (i.e. long-wavelength) light the retinene was released in the all-*trans* form.

In the *synthesis* of cattle rhodopsin, however, the neo-b isomer of retinene is required, a fact which strongly suggests that the retinene moiety of this rhodopsin molecule is in the neo-b form. At some stage in the bleaching process, therefore, conversion of the retinene moiety from the neo-b to the all-*trans* structure occurs. If this conversion is a consequence solely of the absorption of light, then it cannot happen at the indicator yellow (retinene-protein) or retinene stages of the bleaching process for neither of these appreciably absorb orange light. It must occur in circumstances where orange light is fairly strongly absorbed, viz. at the transient orange stage or even

147

during the initial photochemical change from rhodopsin to transient orange (cf. Chap. 4, p. 124).

– – – AND IN BLEACHED SOLUTIONS OF OTHER VISUAL PIGMENTS

The regeneration phenomena just described and the conclusions drawn therefrom apply to cattle rhodopsin, though there is a strong

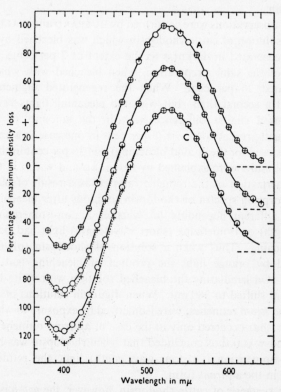

FIG. 5.8. Dependence of the negative portion of the carp (pigment 523) difference spectrum on the wavelength of the bleaching light. (A) ○, changes caused by 21 hr exposure to violet light (430 mμ); +, total changes caused by this and by an additional 18 hr exposure to red light (630 mμ). (B) +, changes caused by 19 hr exposure to the red light; ○, total changes caused by this and by an additional 18 hr exposure to the violet light; data displaced 30 ordinate units from (a). (C) +, changes caused by 2 hr exposure to green light (530 mμ); ○, total changes caused by this and by an additional 18 hr exposure to the violet light. Data displaced 60 ordinate units from (a). pH 8·2, $T = 20°C$.

(*Crescitelli and Dartnall*, 1954)

148

presumption that frog rhodopsin behaves similarly. Unfortunately little work to date has been carried out with visual pigments from other species. It would be dangerous to assume that other visual pigments, or, even, that 'rhodopsins' from other species, behave in a strictly parallel fashion.

CRESCITELLI and DARTNALL (1954) reported some comparable phenomena in visual pigment solutions from the carp. They first established, by the method of partial bleaching (Chap. 6), that their solutions contained a single photosensitive pigment having its absorption maximum at 523 mμ.

The difference spectra obtained by bleaching alkaline solutions of this pigment showed slight, but definite, variations in the negative portions depending on the wavelength of the light used for bleaching. Furthermore, solutions exhaustively bleached with either red (630 mμ) or green (530 mμ) light (see Fig. 5.8) suffered slight additional density losses, maximal at about 420 mμ, when subsequently exposed to short wavelength light. If, however, a solution was first exhaustively bleached with short wavelength light (430 mμ), then no further changes occurred when it was afterwards exposed to light of long wavelength. To this extent, the solutions behaved in a manner strictly analogous to those of frog or cattle rhodopsin. Here the resemblance ceased, however. For it was found that regeneration occurred most readily after exposure to light of long wavelength— the very reverse of what happens with frog and cattle rhodopsin. In the case of the carp pigment, therefore, the product of bleaching is already suitable for regeneration. Isomerization of the photoproduct by light of short wavelength results in the production of less active forms. The regenerated pigment is apparently identical with the original one as is shown in Fig. 5.9 in which the difference spectra for bleaching and for regeneration are compared. It will be noticed from Fig. 5.9 that the negative portions of the two difference spectra are quite different and reproduce in an exaggerated form the differences found between bleachings with long and short wavelength light (Fig. 5.8). The negative portion of the regeneration difference spectrum shows that regeneration occurs from a photoproduct having a greater extinction than the average isomerized product of bleaching. This may indicate that the carp pigment—visual pigment 523— requires an all-*trans* isomer (of retinene$_2$) for its synthesis. However, WALD (1953) states 'the bleaching of porphyropsin yields what is apparently the all-*trans* isomer of retinene$_2$. This is inactive in

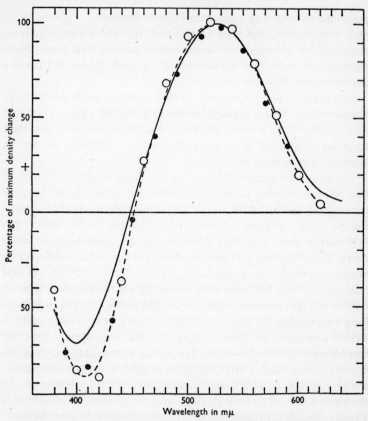

FIG. 5.9. Comparison between the regeneration and bleaching difference spectra of the carp pigment (523). Full-line curve, bleaching difference spectrum; dashed-line curve, regeneration difference spectrum: ○, measurements made from 380 to 620 mμ; ●, return measurements from 590 to 390 mμ. $T = 20°C$.

(*Crescitelli and Dartnall*, 1954)

resynthesizing porphyropsin.' But no experimental details are given and the species from which 'porphyropsin' was obtained is not stated.

CIS-TRANS ISOMERISM IN OTHER VISUAL PIGMENTS

We have seen (p. 144 *et seq*.) that for the synthesis of cattle rhodopsin, a specific isomer of retinene$_1$—*neo*-retinene$_1$ *b*—is required.

150

The only other isomer which combines with cattle opsin is *iso*-retinene$_1$ *a*. But in this case, a new photosensitive pigment, having λ_{max} at 487 mμ is formed. This new pigment, *iso*-rhodopsin, has not been identified with any naturally-occurring visual pigment. WALD regards it, for the present, as an artifact.

Recently, WALD and his colleagues have briefly reported the results of parallel experiments with other visual pigments. The experimental details of these researches have not yet been published in full.

PORPHYROPSIN

The first of these researches concerns porphyropsin the 'purple light-sensitive pigment, associated characteristically with the rods of vertebrates which originate in fresh water—freshwater fishes, lampreys, and certain larval and adult amphibia' (WALD 1953a). Referring to unpublished work in collaboration with BROWN and SMITH, WALD (1953a) writes, 'the bleaching of porphyropsin yields what is apparently the all-*trans* isomer of retinene$_2$. This is inactive in re-synthesizing porphyropsin. From a mixture of retinene$_2$ isomers, however, we have isolated two active fractions, which appear to contain two *cis* isomers of retinene$_2$, which can for the present be called *cis*$_1$ and *cis*$_2$. Neither has been completely purified or crystallized. The *cis*$_1$ fraction, incubated in the dark with a solution of opsin from a fresh-water fish, yields porphyropsin (λ_{max} 523 mμ). The *cis*$_2$ fraction, treated similarly, yields a comparable pigment with λ_{max} 507 mμ; this is *iso*-porphyropsin.' WALD, BROWN and SMITH (cited by WALD, 1953a) found that the active retinene$_2$ isomers would also combine with cattle opsin to form photosensitive pigments. With cattle opsin, however, the spectra of the synthesized pigments were displaced to shorter wavelengths than in the case of fish opsin, viz. maxima at 517 mμ (*cis*$_1$ isomer) and 501 mμ (*cis*$_2$ isomer). Since the absorption spectrum of cattle rhodopsin (λ_{max} 498 mμ) is similarly displaced from frog rhodopsin (λ_{max} 502 mμ) WALD (1953a) considers these experiments show that 'the opsins are so closely related in the rhodopsin and porphyropsin systems that it seems proper to regard them as belonging to the same family, the scotopsins. The rhodopsin and porphyropsin systems therefore share throughout the same proteins; it is only their carotenoids which differ' (WALD, 1953a).

151

IODOPSIN

WALD, BROWN and SMITH (1952) have also given brief details of experiments with iodopsin, the photosensitive pigment (λ_{max} 562 mμ) found, together with rhodopsin in the chicken retina (WALD, 1937, BLISS, 1946). According to them the bleaching of iodopsin, like that of rhodopsin, yields an inactive isomer of retinene$_1$, apparently the all-*trans* isomer. The synthesis of iodopsin from retinene and chicken opsin, however, requires a different isomer of retinene$_1$, namely *neo*-retinene *b*, the same isomer as is required for cattle rhodopsin. 'The carotenoids of the rhodopsin and iodopsin systems are therefore identical; only the proteins are different. The cone protein [i.e. chicken opsin] can be called *photopsin* to distinguish it from the *scotopsins* of the rods.' In a later paper WALD (1953a) reports that 'just as *iso*-retinene *a* yields *iso*-rhodopsin when incubated with scotopsin, it yields a similarly displaced pigment, *iso*-iodopsin, on incubation with photopsin. The λ_{max} of *iso*-iodopsin is at about 515 mμ.'

CYANOPSIN

One of the isomers of retinene$_1$ (*neo*-retinene *b*) combines with 'scotopsin' to form rhodopsin; the same isomer with 'photopsin' forms iodopsin. Similarly, one of the isomers of retinene$_2$ combines with 'scotopsin' to form porphyropsin; what would be the result of combining the same isomer of retinene$_2$ with *photopsin*? In order to answer this question, WALD, BROWN and SMITH (1953) first exposed a digitonin extract of dark adapted chicken retinae (iodopsin and rhodopsin) to deep red light. This light hardly affected the rhodopsin in the extract but bleached the iodopsin to retinene$_1$ and chicken opsin (photopsin). Since the retinene$_1$ was produced in the inactive all-*trans* form there was no danger of recombination with the protein (regeneration of iodopsin). A small amount of cis_1-retinene$_2$ in digitonin solution was now added to the extract which was then left in darkness for 8 min to allow combination between the cis_1-retinene$_2$ and photopsin to occur.

At the end of this period the absorption spectrum of the mixture was measured, and again after it had been exposed for $4\frac{1}{2}$ min to deep red light. The difference between these two sets of measurements is shown by the difference spectrum in Fig. 5.10. This is the difference spectrum of a new visual pigment (cyanopsin) formed by the combination of cis_1-retinene$_2$ and photopsin. Unfortunately WALD did not test the homogeneity of cyanopsin. Moreover in view of the number of 'passengers' in the experiment, viz. chicken rhodopsin, chicken iodopsin not bleached by the original exposure to deep red

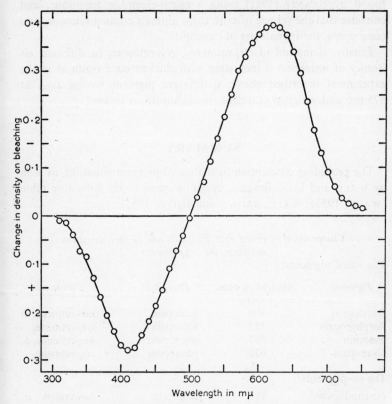

FIG. 5.10. The difference spectrum of cyanopsin, a photosensitive pigment formed from the opsin of chicken iodopsin and an isomer of retinene$_2$ (cis$_1$).
(*After Wald, Brown and Smith,* 1953)

light, and any pigment regenerated from the products of the original bleaching, the purity of cyanopsin may be questioned.

WALD, BROWN and SMITH (1953) consider that cyanopsin would probably occur in any retina which contains vitamin A$_2$ or retinene$_2$ and cone opsin. They attribute the fact that cyanopsin, as such, has not been demonstrated in a retinal extract to the common practice of making extracts by red light—which would, of course bleach any cyanopsin present. They showed that the absorption spectrum of cyanopsin bears a close resemblance to the photopic sensitivity curves of the tortoise (*testudo graeca*) and the tench (*tinca tinca*) as found by GRANIT (1941) using a micro-electrode technique, and consider that the retinae of both these animals contain retinene$_2$ and cone opsin, the ingredients of cyanopsin.

Finally, if instead of cis_1 retinene$_2$, cis_2-retinene$_2$ (a different *cis* isomer of retinene$_2$) is incubated with chicken cone opsin as in the experiment described above, a different pigment having λ_{max} at 575 mμ and which WALD calls *iso*-cyanopsin, is formed.

SUMMARY

The preceding description of the visual pigment situation, as seen by WALD and his colleagues, is summarized in the following table (WALD, 1953a, WALD, BROWN and SMITH, 1953).

Composition of visual photopigments and of their cis-trans
artifacts, the iso *pigments*

The visual pigments:

Pigment	Absorption max. (mμ)	Protein	Carotenoid
Rhodopsin	500	scotopsin	*neo*-retinene$_1$ *b*
Porphyropsin	522	scotopsin	cis_1-retinene$_2$
Iodopsin	562	photopsin	*neo*-retinene$_1$ *b*
Cyanopsin	620	photopsin	cis_1-retinene$_2$

The *iso*-pigments:

Iso-rhodopsin	487	scotopsin	*iso*-retinene$_1$ *a*
Iso-porphyropsin	507	scotopsin	cis_2-retinene$_2$
Iso-iodopsin	515	photopsin	*iso*-retinene$_1$ *a*
Iso-cyanopsin	575	photopsin	cis_2-retinene$_2$

The scheme of this table gives an impression of universality which is not yet warranted. For example it implies that 'rhodopsin'—whatever its source—is derived from *neo*-retinene$_1$ *b* and scotopsin. In fact, this has been established only for cattle rhodopsin. Other retinene$_1$ isomers—inactive as regards cattle opsin—might well be active with opsins of other animals. Similarly, the data given for 'porphyropsin' were obtained 'using opsin from a fresh-water fish' (WALD, 1953a). The extrapolation of this result to embrace all such species is premature, particularly since the 'porphyropsin' band is centred at a wavelength which, in different fresh-water fish, varies at least from 520 to 533 mμ (see Chap. 2). Again, iodopsin, a presumptive cone pigment which, to date, has been found only in chicken retinae (WALD, 1937, BLISS, 1941) is, in the table, so related to rhodopsin as to imply that all retinae containing it, contain iodopsin also—provided that retinal cones (and hence 'photopsin') are present. Similarly with cyanopsin and porphyropsin.

In effect the table *combines* the results of the experiments on *cis-trans* isomerism with WALD's earlier conclusion (Chap. 2) that there are only two rod pigments—rhodopsin and porphyropsin, based respectively on 'retinene$_1$' and 'retinene$_2$.' Now that it has been shown that retinene$_1$ (for example) can exist in several *cis-trans* forms —all of which give the *same* Carr-Price reaction the validity of the earlier conclusion is questionable (cf. Chap. 2, p. 38 *et seq.*). Nevertheless even in 1953b WALD wrote 'in the rods of vertebrates there is substantial evidence for the existence of only two visual pigments, rhodopsin and porphyropsin. The distribution of these pigments has been explored to the point at which it begins to seem probable that there are no others. On the other hand, iodopsin marks only a beginning with the visual pigments of vertebrate cones. More pigments than this are needed, if only to provide a basis for colour vision in animals.'

But if more cone pigments than iodopsin (and cyanopsin) are necessary, how are we to envisage their composition? If, for example, a new cone pigment based on a retinene$_1$ isomer were discovered, how would it modify the table? One would have to suppose either that the pigment contained a protein different from 'photopsin,' or a retinene$_1$ isomer different from *neo-b* or *iso-a*. In either case a difficulty arises. For the one supposition destroys the scotopsin-photopsin conception and the other endangers the rhodopsin-porphyropsin theory (because the new retinene$_1$ isomer would, presumably, combine with a scotopsin to form a new rod pigment).

In the next chapter we review the results of some homogeneity tests which give illustrative point to these remarks.

REFERENCES

BALL, S., GOODWIN, T. W. and MORTON, R. A. (1948). Studies on vitamin A. 5: The preparation of retinene$_1$–vitamin A aldehyde. *Biochem. J.*, **42**, 516–523.

BLISS, A. F. (1946). The chemistry of daylight vision. *J. gen. Physiol.*, **29**, 277–297.

BRAUDE, E. A., JONES, E. R. H., KOCH, H. P., RICHARDSON, R. W., SONDHEIMER, F. and TOOGOOD, J. B. (1949). Studies in light absorption. Part VI: Steric inhibition of resonance in natural and synthetic derivatives of *cyclo* hexene. *J. chem. Soc.*, 1890–1897.

CHASE, A. M. (1937). An accessory photosensitive substance in visual purple regeneration. *Science*, **85**, 484.

CHASE, A. M. and SMITH, E. L. (1939). Regeneration of visual purple in solution. *J. gen. Physiol.*, **23**, 21–39.

COLLINS, F. D. and MORTON, R. A. (1950). Studies in rhodopsin. 3: Rhodopsin and transient orange. *Biochem. J.*, **47**, 18–24.

CRESCITELLI, F. and DARTNALL, H. J. A. (1954). A photosensitive pigment of the carp retina. *J. Physiol.*, **125**, 607–627.

DALVI, P. D. and MORTON, R. A. (1952). Preparation of *neo*vitamin A esters and *neo*retinene$_1$. *Biochem. J.*, **50**, 43–48.

GARBERS, C. F., EUGSTER, C. H. and KARRER, P. (1952). Carotinoidsynthesen X. Weitere stereoisomere 1,18-Diphenyl-3,7,12,16-tetramethyloctadecanonaene. Zugleich ein Beitrag zu *L. Pauling's* Theorie der sterischen Hinderung bei *cis-trans*-isomeren Polyenen. *Helv. Chim. Acta.*, **35**, 1850–1864.

GOODWIN, T. W. (1953). The biogenesis of carotenoids. *J. Sci. Food Agric.*, 209–220.

GRANIT, R. (1941). A relation between rod and cone substances, based on scotopic and photopic spectra of *cyprinus, tinca, anguilla* and *testudo. Acta physiol. scand.*, **2**, 334–346.

HENBEST, H. B. and WOODS, G. (1952). Studies in the polyene series. Part XL: Preparation and properties of 2-acetyl-1:3:3-trimethyl *cyclo* hexene. *J. chem. Soc.*, 1150–1154.

HUBBARD, R., GREGERMAN, R. I. and WALD, G. (1953). Geometrical isomers of retinene. *J. gen. Physiol.*, **36**, 415–429.

HUBBARD, R. and WALD, G. (1951). The mechanism of rhodopsin synthesis. *Proc. natl. Acad. Sci. Wash.*, **37**, 69–79.

HUBBARD, R. and WALD, G. (1952). *Cis-trans* isomers of vitamin A and retinene in the rhodopsin system. *J. gen. Physiol.*, **36**, 269–315.

KLYNE, W. (1954). *Progress in stereochemistry* 1. Ed. by KLYNE, W. London, Butterworth's scientific publications.

LEWIS, G. N. and CALVIN, M. (1939). The colour of organic substances. *Chem. Rev.*, **25**, 273–328.

OROSHNIK, W., KARMAS, G. and MEBANE, A. D. (1952). Synthesis of polyenes. 1: *Retro* vitamin A methyl ether. Spectral relationships between the β-ionylidene and *retro*ionylidene series. *J. Am. chem. Soc.*, **74**, 295–304.

PAULING, L. (1939). Recent work on the configuration and electronic structure of molecules; with some applications to natural products. *Fortschr. Chem. org. Naturstoffe*, **3**, 203–235

ROBESON, C. D. and BAXTER, J. G. (1947). *Neo*vitamin A. *J. Am. chem. Soc.*, **69**, 136–141.

STANLEY, W. M. and ADAMS, R. (1929). Stereochemistry of diphenyl compounds. The resolution of 2.2'-dihydroxy-3.3'-dicarboxy-1.1'-dinaphthyl III. *Rec. Trav. chim.*, **48**, 1035–1040.

WALD, G. (1937). Photo-labile pigments of the chicken retina. *Nature, Lond.*, **140**, 545–546.

WALD, G. (1953a). Vision. *Fed. Proc.*, **12**, 606–611.

WALD, G. (1953b). The biochemistry of vision. *Ann. Rev. Biochem.*, **22**, 497–526.

WALD, G. and BROWN, P. K. (1953). The molar extinction of rhodopsin. *J. gen. Physiol.*, **37**, 189–200.

WALD, G., BROWN, P. K. and SMITH, P. H. (1952). Iodopsin. *Fed. Proc.*, **11**, 304.

WALD, G., BROWN, P. K. and SMITH, P. H. (1953). Cyanopsin, a new cone pigment of vision. *Science*, **118**, 505–508.

ZECHMEISTER, L. (1944). *Cis-trans* isomerization and stereochemistry of carotenoids and diphenylpolyenes. *Chem. Rev.*, **34**, 267–344.

CHAPTER SIX

The Homogeneity of Visual Pigment Solutions

In 1949 DARTNALL was attempting to estimate the retinal densities of the scotopic pigments in various animals. Having done this for the frog, a representative of the 'rhodopsin' class, he then decided to examine a representative of the 'porphyropsin' class. The tench was chosen since its scotopic sensitivity had been measured (GRANIT, 1941).

Aqueous digitonin extracts of dark-adapted tench retinae were, therefore, prepared (DARTNALL, 1950, 1952a). On exposing these extracts to light it was found, however, that bleaching was maximal at approximately 520 mμ instead of at 535–540 mμ as reported for the tench by KÖTTGEN and ABELSDORFF (1896) and by BAYLISS, LYTHGOE and TANSLEY (1936). On the other hand a similar extract made from another fresh-water fish—the pike—behaved in the expected way.

DARTNALL'S (1952a) results are shown in Fig. 6.1. The density spectra, before and after bleaching, of the pike extract are given in the upper half of the figure. The λ_{max} of the unbleached solution was 530 mμ. The difference spectrum—obtained by subtracting the 'bleached' curve from the 'unbleached' shows that, on bleaching the solution, density was lost maximally at 535 mμ and gained maximally at 405 mμ. Such behaviour is generally accepted as typical of a 'porphyropsin' (visual violet) preparation (WALD, 1939b). The loss in density was due to bleaching of the visual pigment and the gain, to the consequent formation of a photoproduct having λ_{max} about 405 mμ.

The density spectra, before and after bleaching, of a tench extract which had been prepared in exactly the same way are given in the lower half of Fig. 6.1. The 'unbleached' curve had λ_{max} at 495 mμ instead of at 530 mμ as in the pike.

The dissimilarity between the pike and tench extracts is best shown,

158

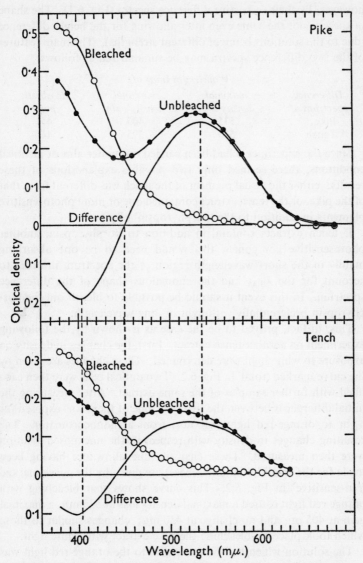

Fig. 6.1. Comparison between the density spectra of pike and tench extracts, before and after total bleaching by white light. The vertical dashed lines facilitate comparison of the two difference spectra. Pike extract, pH 8·24; tench extract, pH 8·40; $T = 20°C$.

(*Dartnall*, 1952a)

however, by their respective difference spectra (Fig. 6.1). The shape of these is not the same even after allowing for the height difference (due to the solutions being of different strengths). The main features of the two difference spectra may be summarized as follows:

	Wavelength (mμ) of		
Difference spectrum of	*maximal density loss*	*maximal density gain*	*Isosbestic point*
Pike	535	405	451
Tench	520	395	440

Since the experiments had been carried out under almost identical conditions, there seemed only two possible explanations of these results: either the visual pigment of the tench was different from that of the pike, or the tench extract contained one or more photosensitive pigments in addition to the 'porphyropsin' of pike.

If tench extracts contain, in addition to porphyropsin, another photosensitive component this would need to be one absorbing mainly in the short wavelength region of the spectrum in order to account for the λ_{max} and the anomalous shape of the difference spectrum. In this event it should be possible to bleach out the porphyropsin preferentially with light of long wavelength.

This, in fact, proved to be the case as is shown by the following experiment on another tench extract. First, the changes in density on exposure to white light were determined. These changes are given by the curve marked 'total' in Fig. 6.2. Two optical cells were then each filled with further samples of the same extract. After measuring the initial differences between the two cells, one of them was exposed for $4\frac{1}{4}$ hr to orange-red light (610 mμ) from a monochromator. The resulting changes in density with respect to the unexposed solution were then measured. These changes (due allowance having been made for the small initial differences) are given by the curve marked 'red-sensitive' in Fig. 6.2. This curve shows that bleaching with orange red light caused a maximal density loss at 535 mμ, a maximal gain at 405 mμ and no change at 450 mμ; changes similar to those which took place on bleaching the pike extract with white light.

The solution which had been exposed to the orange-red light was then exposed to green light (530 mμ) for 30 min. The object of this was to bleach any traces of the red-sensitive component which might still have remained. In the event, measurement showed that there was no further loss of density at 535 mμ, but only a very small amount of bleaching in the short wavelength region of the spectrum maximal (density loss at 470 mμ, 0·003). The solution was therefore exposed to white light for 15 min. This caused considerable further bleaching, maximal at 470 mμ (density loss 0·026). The changes in

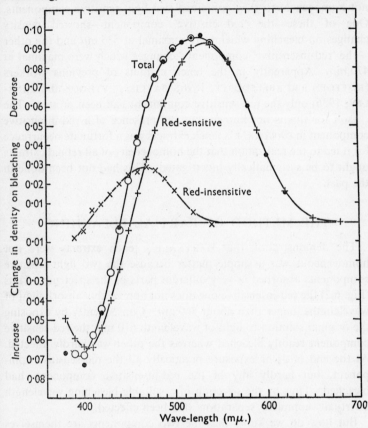

FIG. 6.2. The two light-sensitive components in tench extracts. ●, changes on exposure to white light ('total'); +, changes on exposure of another sample of the same extract to light of wavelength 610 mμ ('red-sensitive'); ×, further changes on exposure to short-wave light ('red-insensitive'); ○, algebraic sum of red-sensitive and red-insensitive components. pH 8·66, $T = 20$°C.

(*Dartnall*, 1952a)

density due to the exposures to green and white light are given by the curve marked 'red-insensitive' in Fig. 6.2. The algebraic sum of the difference spectra of the red-sensitive and red-insensitive components of the extract is also shown in Fig. 6.2, and is in good agreement with

161

the 'total' difference spectrum which had been obtained by bleaching another sample in a single exposure to white light.

These experiments showed that the extracts of tench retinae were not homogeneous; they contained two light-sensitive components. One of these—the 'red-sensitive' component—showed density changes on bleaching which were maximal at 535 mμ and the other —the 'red-insensitive' component—changes which were maximal at 470 mμ. Apparently in the tench extracts of previous workers (KÖTTGEN and ABELSDORFF, 1896; BAYLISS, LYTHGOE and TANSLEY, 1936) only the red-sensitive component had been present. The reason for this is not known, but the presence of a red-insensitive component in DARTNALL'S tench extracts was a fortunate occurrence for it led to the realization that the homogeneity of all retinal extracts ought to be systematically investigated. This had not been done in the past.

THE METHOD OF PARTIAL BLEACHING

The demonstration that DARTNALL'S tench extracts were not homogeneous was a simple matter because the two light-sensitive components absorbed in very different parts of the spectrum. Thus (Fig. 6.2) the red-insensitive one does not appreciably absorb light of wavelengths longer than about 560 mμ. Consequently by exposing the original solution to light of wavelength 610 mμ, the red-sensitive component readily bleached whereas the other was hardly affected. At the end of $4\frac{1}{4}$ hr exposure practically all the red-sensitive component, but hardly any of the red-insensitive component, had bleached. Thus by the selection of a suitable bleaching wavelength a virtually complete 'separation' had been effected.

But how do we know that the two components are themselves homogeneous? May they not both be a mixture of pigments—red-sensitive in the one case and red-insensitive in the other? The experiment just described throws no light on these questions. Both components had been completely bleached, the one by orange-red light, and then the other by white light. Just as the total bleaching of the tench extract (Fig. 6.1) yielded no information about the homogeneity of the extract, so the total bleaching of each of its two components tells us nothing of their individual make-up. Clearly, the test of partial bleaching, which disclosed the heterogeneity of the extract as a whole, can be applied also to its components.

We may define a homogeneous photopigment as one which yields the same results (difference spectrum) when bleached—no matter what the spectral composition of the bleaching light, nor what proportion of the photopigment is affected. Every instalment of photo-chemical bleaching—however caused—must be identical, after allowance for the magnitude of the instalment has been made, e.g. by expressing the difference spectra on a percentage basis.

The results of a typical experiment which illustrates this test of homogeneity are shown in Fig. 6.3 (A). Curve 1 represents the original density spectrum of an unexposed extract prepared from carp retinae. After 3 hr exposure to violet light (430 mμ) from a monochromator, the density spectrum changed to curve 2. At this stage in the experiment the solution was left undisturbed in darkness for 18 hr, but this resulted in no significant changes. The solution was then exposed to red light (630 mμ) for 1 hr which caused bleaching to curve 3. This was followed by a 1-hr exposure to green light (530 mμ) which caused further bleaching to curve 4. At this stage the experiment was interrupted once more, the solution remaining in darkness for 22 hr. During this period considerable regeneration of the photopigment took place (curve 5). Finally the solution was exposed to white light to complete the bleaching (curve 6). Difference spectra constructed from these results are shown in Fig. 6.3 (B). They form a family of similarly-shaped curves. Several experiments of this type were carried out. In all cases the difference spectra obtained—when plotted with their maxima equally scaled—were practically identical, showing that the extracts contained only one photosensitive pigment.

In this instance it is fairly easy to interpret the results obtained. The same applies, also, in a case, like that of the tench, where there is a mixture of two components absorbing in widely separated parts of the spectrum. It is then possible to subject the component which absorbs in the longer wavelength regions to the partial bleaching test of homogeneity, without introducing serious complications due to concurrent bleaching of the other component. When all of the red-sensitive component has been removed, the other component can be likewise examined.

It may happen, however, that in a binary mixture there is a considerable 'overlap' between the density spectra of the two photopigments. It would thus be impossible to bleach one pigment without affecting the other. In such a case a sharp 'separation' cannot be

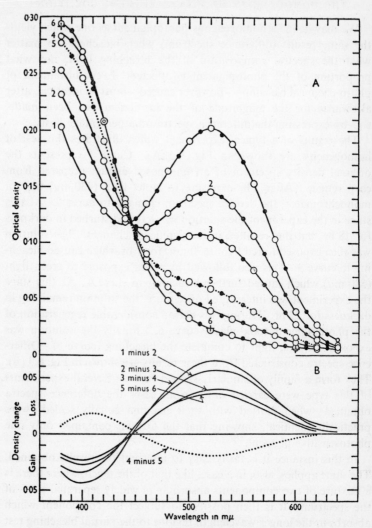

Fig. 6.3. (A) A typical partial bleaching experiment (carp extract, pH 8·24, $T = 20°C$). Curve 1, original density spectrum; curve 2, after 3 hr exposure to violet light (430 mμ)—unchanged after 18 hr in darkness; curve 3, after 1 hr further exposure to red light (630 mμ); curve 4, after 1 hr further exposure to green light (530 mμ); curve 5, after 22 hr in darkness; curve 6, after 10 min exposure to white light. ○, measurements made consecutively from 380 to 640 mμ; ●, return measurements from 630 to 390 mμ. (B) Difference spectra, formed from the data of (A) by subtracting the density spectrum at any stage from that for the preceding stage.

(*Crescitelli and Dartnall*, 1954)

obtained and it is necessary to analyse the results. The factors involved in such an analysis may be best considered with reference to simple theory.

THEORY OF THE BLEACHING OF A BINARY MIXTURE

Provided the optical density is small, the complex equation describing the bleaching kinetics of visual purple (Chap. 3, equation 16) may be replaced by,

$$\log_e c_0/c_t = \alpha\gamma It \qquad (1)$$

or, in the alternative exponential form

$$c_t = c_0 \cdot e^{-\alpha\gamma It} \qquad (2)$$

In these equations, c_0 is the initial concentration of visual purple and c_t, that after t sec exposure to the bleaching light. The symbols α, γ and I were defined in Chap. 3, p. 68.

The errors involved in the use of equations (1) or (2) instead of the more exact one, are less than 5 per cent provided the optical density ($\log_{10} I/I_t$) of the solution does not exceed 0·12 at the bleaching wavelength.

Equation (2) shows that the proportion of visual purple remaining (c_t/c_0) at any time during the course of the bleaching is exponentially related to the time of exposure. The kinetics of bleaching thus follow the law of organic growth (or decay) and hence resemble those of unimolecular reactions or of the decay of radioactive substances. The reason for this lies in the fact that the amount of light absorbed by a solution is proportional to its density—when this is small (Chap. 1, p. 19). Since the rate of bleaching is proportional to the light absorbed, and since the optical density is proportional to the concentration, we have the rate determined by the concentration—a necessary condition for the law of organic growth to apply.

In Fig. 6.4, c_t/c_0, expressed as a percentage, is plotted against a time scale for a number of values (100, 50, 25, 10 and 1) of the parameter $\alpha\gamma I$. The family of curves shown can be interpreted as follows.

In the first instance we may regard $\alpha\gamma$ as invariable, in which case the family represents the time courses of bleachings in various intensities of light of a constant wavelength. Inspection of the curves in Fig. 6.4 then shows that doubling the intensity (for example) halves the time required to reach a given degree of bleaching. The amount of bleaching is thus governed by the product of time and intensity, that is by the quantum dosage received by the solution.

Alternatively, we may assume the intensity, I, to be constant and regard the parameter variation as due entirely to variation in the photosensitivity, $\alpha\gamma$; or, since γ is constant in any case, to variation in α, the extinction coefficient. The family of curves in Fig. 6.4 then

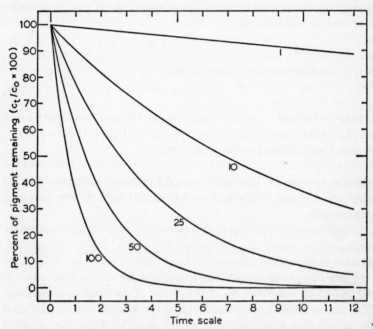

FIG. 6.4. The time courses of bleaching of the visual pigments. Curves calculated according to the equation $c_t/c_0 = e^{-\alpha\gamma It}$ for various values of the parameter $\alpha\gamma I$ between 1 and 100.

gives the time courses of bleaching caused by lights of different regions of an equal quantum-intensity spectrum. The curves demonstrate that the time to effect a given degree of bleaching is inversely proportional to the extinction coefficient of the photopigment.

Visual purple is the only one of the visual pigments whose photochemical bleaching has been investigated in much detail. However, BLISS (1946) has shown that iodopsin behaves similarly. Assuming that the bleaching kinetics of visual purple is a pattern for all visual pigments, we can consider the bleaching of a mixture of (say) two photopigments.

In a mixture there is 'competition' between the photopigments for the light. The total amount of light absorbed by the mixture is always less than the sum of those amounts which would be separately absorbed by either pigment in the absence of the other. For example, if either pigment separately absorbed 90 per cent (density $= 1$) of the incident light, the two together would absorb 99 per cent (density $= 2$), each pigment when in admixture capturing only $49\frac{1}{2}$ per cent. However, provided the total density of the solution at the bleaching wavelength does not exceed 0·12, the amount of light absorbed by the mixture falls short of the sum of those amounts which would be separately absorbed by less than 5 per cent. In such cases the partitioning of the total light absorbed between the two pigments in proportion to their optical densities results in each absorbing very nearly as much light when in admixture as it would have done in the absence of the other. Thus, in solutions of low optical density, each pigment bleaches at practically the same rate as it would if it were alone in the solution.

Let us suppose that the mixture is exposed to a bleaching light of wavelength such that the photosensitivities of the two pigments are not the same. One pigment therefore bleaches faster than the other and consequently, if the bleaching is interrupted at any stage, the unbleached fraction is relatively richer in the less photosensitive pigment than was the original solution.

In Fig. 6.4 let curve 100 represent the time course of bleaching of the more photosensitive pigment P_1, and curve 10 that of the less (P_2). Then after time 1, 36 per cent of P_1 remains in solution and 90 per cent of P_2. Thus one time unit of bleaching increases the ratio of P_2 to P_1 in the unbleached fraction (compared with that of the original solution) by a factor of $90/36 = 2\cdot5$. At a later period, say time 5, 0·5 per cent of P_1 and 60 per cent of P_2 remain, the enrichment factor thus advancing to 120 as a result of the longer bleaching period. Obviously, the longer the bleaching is allowed to proceed, the closer does the unbleached fraction approximate to pure P_2. It is relatively easy, therefore, to obtain 'pure' data for the less photosensitive pigment. Thus, even supposing the original solution contained 10 parts of P_1 to only 1 part of P_2, then by bleaching for time 5 (Fig. 6.4), the unbleached residue would contain 0·05 of P_1 and 0·6 of P_2, i.e. over 90 per cent of P_2.

Let us now consider the bleached fraction. After time 1 (Fig. 6.4), 64 per cent of P_1 has bleached and 10 per cent of P_2. Thus one time unit yields a bleached fraction having a P_1/P_2 ratio 6·4 times that of the original solution. At time 5, the enrichment factor is 99·5/40, only $2\frac{1}{2}$; at time $\frac{1}{2}$ it is 40/5 = 8. The maximum possible value of the enrichment ratio in the bleached fraction is obviously equal to the ratio of the photosensitivities of the two pigments, i.e. 10 in the present

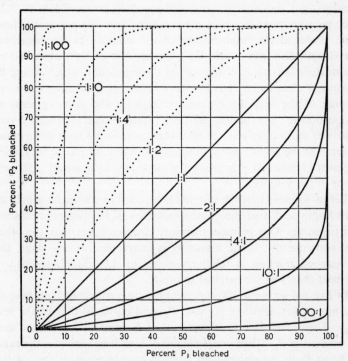

FIG. 6.5. Relation between the percentage amounts bleached of two pigments in a binary mixture. Curves are shown for various ratios of the photosensitivity of P_1 to that of P_2.

case. This maximum is only achieved in a vanishingly-small amount of bleaching. For this reason, the characterization of the more photosensitive pigment is generally difficult. Thus, if, for example, the original solution contained 1 part of P_1 and 10 parts of P_2, the best difference spectrum for P_1 which could be obtained, given a photosensitivity ratio of 10:1, would consist of equal contributions from P_1 and P_2.

In Fig. 6.5 (constructed from the curves of Fig. 6.4), the relation between the percentage amounts bleached of two pigments, P_1 and

P_2, in admixture are shown graphically. Each curve refers, as indicated, to a given photosensitivity ratio (determined by the wavelength of the bleaching light). When the ratio is unity it is impossible, of course, to achieve any separation by bleaching. This is shown in Fig. 6.5 by the line, marked '1:1,' having equal ordinate and abscissa values. For other ratios, separation is possible to a greater or less degree. The whole family of curves, some of which are drawn in Fig. 6.5, is symmetrical about the line '1:1.' Thus the curve labelled '100:1' is the counterpart of that labelled '1:100,' and so on.

SOME RESULTS OBTAINED BY PARTIAL BLEACHING

A BINARY MIXTURE

In a recent investigation BRIDGES (1955) found that visual pigment solutions prepared from rainbow trout (*Salmo irideus*) were not homogeneous. On exposing the solutions to monochromatic light of long wavelength bleaching was, at first, maximal at about 532 mμ. As bleaching continued, however, the λ_{max} of the difference spectra obtained shifted to shorter and shorter wavelengths. After prolonged exposure to the long-wave bleaching light, only about one-half of the total photosensitive material was bleached. The less-sensitive residue was readily bleached, however, by employing a bleaching light of short wavelength.

The results of one of the partial bleaching experiments are set out in the following table.

Bleaching conditions	λ_{max} of difference spectrum	Density loss at λ_{max}
1. 35 min, $\lambda = 650$ mμ	532 mμ	0·0228
2. 35 min, $\lambda = 650$ mμ	529 mμ	0·0141
3. 14 hr, $\lambda = 670$ mμ	522 mμ	0·0304
4. 35 min, $\lambda = 650$ mμ	515 mμ	0·0040
5. 25 min, $\lambda = 580$ mμ	507 mμ	0·0207
6. 10 min, white light	507 mμ	0·0380

From these, and other similar experiments, BRIDGES concluded that the rainbow trout solutions contained a mixture of two photosensitive pigments: one with λ_{max} at 533 mμ, and apparently identical with the visual pigment 533 of tench, pike and bleak (DARTNALL, 1952a, 1955) the other with λ_{max} at 507 mμ and similar to, if not identical with, the visual pigment 510 of bleak. It was relatively

169

easy to establish the homogeneity of the 'red-insensitive' 507 pigment: by prolonged exposure to long-wave light all, or virtually all, of the red-sensitive material was removed, leaving sufficient 507 pigment in the solutions for subsequent examination. But it was not possible to bleach the 'red-sensitive' component of the mixture without bleaching a little of the 507 pigment at the same time. Consequently all the difference spectra for the red-sensitive component (1–4 in table) were 'contaminated' by contributions from pigment 507.

We can check whether the tabulated data conform with the conclusion that the solutions contained a mixture of pigments 533 and 507 by applying the theory of bleaching of a binary mixture developed in the previous pages. In the first instance, by adding together, in various proportions, curves for the two pigments, a graph relating the λ_{max} of a mixture with its composition can be obtained. From this graph it is found that curves with λ_{max} at 532, 529, 522 and 515 mμ consist of 6, 12½, 33 and 60 per cent of pigment 507 respectively. Applying these results to the data the composition of each difference spectrum can be calculated as follows:

	Pigment 507	Pigment 533
1.	0·0014 (1·9%)	0·0214 (38%)
2.	0·0018 (4·3%)	0·0123 (60%)
3.	0·0100 (17·8%)	0·0204 (97%)
4.	0·0024 (21%)	0·0016 (100%)
5.	0·0207 (49%)	— (100%)
6.	0·0380 (100%)	— (100%)
	0·0743	0·0557

The figures in brackets give the cumulative percentages bleached at each stage. When the percentages for one pigment are plotted against those for the other, the resulting curve is one of the family shown in Fig. 6.5, specifically that for a photosensitivity ratio of about 20:1. Finally, since the ratio of pigment 533 to 507 in the original mixture was 0·0557 to 0·0743, i.e. 0·75, we should expect that the best obtainable difference spectrum for pigment 533 (see p. 168) would consist of 20 × 0·75 = 15 parts of 533 and 1 part of 507. Such a mixture would have $\lambda_{max} = 532$ mμ. This was, in fact, the λ_{max} of the first difference spectrum. Thus the difference spectra of the first four bleachings can be simulated by mixtures of pigments 533 and 507; the proportions of the two pigments so required agree with the bleaching of a binary mixture at a photosensitivity ratio of

20; and the highest λ_{max} for a difference spectrum is as expected. In other words the results are consistent with the hypothesis that the solution contained pigments 533 and 507.

A TERNARY MIXTURE

The 'total' difference spectrum obtained by bleaching an extract of tench retinae with white light (Fig. 6.1) had an 'anomalous' shape, owing to visual pigment 467 which was present in the extracts in addition to the expected visual pigment 533. It might be thought from this, that the difference spectrum of a non-homogeneous extract would always have an abnormal shape or an unexpected λ_{max}.

If this were so then the total difference spectra obtained by bleaching to completion with white light would provide a valid and rapid means of surveying the visual pigments of a number of species (cf. the investigation of KÖTTGEN and ABELSDORFF, 1896).

The danger of this assumption is illustrated by the results of an investigation of the visual pigments of the bleak, a common freshwater fish (DARTNALL, 1952b, 1955). When a retinal extract, prepared from this fish, was bleached by white light, a difference spectrum almost identical with that for the pike was obtained (Fig. 6.6). In both cases, the maximum loss of density on bleaching was at 535 mμ, and the maximum gain (due to formation of a photoproduct) was at 400–405. It might have been fairly conjectured, therefore, that the visual pigment of the bleak was the same as that for the pike (pigment 533).

As a careful inspection of Fig. 6.6 shows, however, the two difference spectra are not exactly alike. Had they not been obtained under identical conditions one would hesitate to regard the small differences between them as significant. In the present instance, however, the differences were well outside experimental error. It was decided, therefore, to subject the bleak extracts to a homogeneity test.

Two cells were filled with further samples of the same extract. One cell was exposed to light of dominant wavelength 610 mμ for 1 hr, while the other was kept in darkness under otherwise identical conditions (20°C). The changes in density of the exposed solution were then measured, using the unexposed cell as a 'control.' These changes, maximal at 545 mμ are shown by curve 1 in Fig. 6.7. The cell was then returned to the bleaching apparatus and exposed for a further 2 hr to light of wavelength 610 mμ. The density changes, maximal at 538 mμ, resulting from this second exposure are shown by curve 2 in Fig. 6.7. Finally, to complete the bleaching, the cell was exposed to 'white' light (a 15 W lamp) for 20 min. This caused further density changes, maximal at 512 mμ (curve 3 in Fig. 6.7).

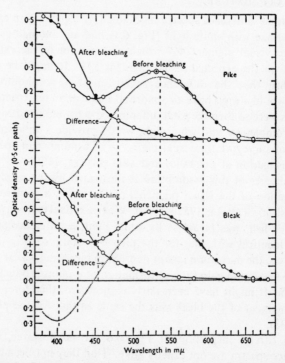

FIG. 6.6. Comparison between the density spectra of pike and bleak extracts, before and after total bleaching by white light. The vertical dashed lines facilitate comparison of the two difference spectra. ○, measurements made consecutively from 380 to 680 mμ; ●, return measurements from 670 to 390 mμ. Pike extract, pH 8·24; bleak extract, pH 8·15; $T = 20°C$.

(*Dartnall*, 1955)

The total density changes caused by the orange-red light (two exposures) and the white light are given by the algebraic sum of the separate density changes, that is by the sum of the curves 1–3 in Fig. 6.7. This sum is represented by the dotted curve. For comparison, the density changes which had been observed on the previous day when an earlier sample of the same extract bleached to completion by a single exposure to white light (see Fig. 6.6) are shown in Fig. 6.7 by the full-line curve.

The small difference between the direct measurements of the total changes (full-line curve in Fig. 6.7) and the sum of the separate changes (dotted curve in Fig. 6.7) are due to thermal decomposition

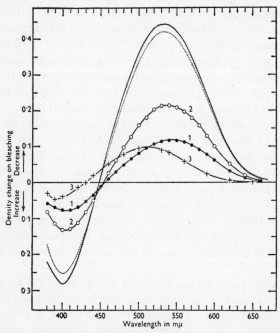

FIG. 6.7. Composite nature of the bleak total difference spectrum. Full-line curve, density changes in a bleak extract when completely bleached by white light. Curve 1 (●), density changes in another sample of the same extract when exposed to orange-red light; curve 2 (○), additional changes on further exposure to the orange-red light; curve 3 (+), additional and final changes on further exposure to white light. Dotted-line curve, algebraic sum of curves 1–3. pH 8·15, $T = 20°C$.

(*Dartnall*, 1955)

of the photosensitive pigments between sampling times (1 day). Apart from this, the summed changes of density agree with the direct changes resulting from a single exposure to white light. This shows that the total end result was not dependent on the mode of bleaching.

The experiments also show that the bleak solutions could be bleached in dissimilar stages. Thus (Fig. 6.7) the density losses were

173

maximal at 545 mμ in the first exposure, at 538 mμ in the second and at 512 mμ in the third. The second exposure yielded a difference spectrum (curve 2 in Fig. 6.7) like that for visual pigment 533, suggesting that this pigment might be a component of the solution. If so, then the difference spectrum which had been obtained by the first exposure to 610 mμ (curve 1 in Fig. 6.7) would certainly have been 'contaminated' by that for visual pigment 533. This would indicate an even longer wavelength than 545 mμ for the true absorption maximum of the first 'pigment.' Similarly the third and final bleaching with white light (curve 3 in Fig. 6.7) would include any visual pigment 533 not removed by the previous exposures to 610 mμ light. In this event, the true absorption maximum of the third 'pigment' would be at a shorter wavelength than 512 mμ.

As in the cases of the tench and the rainbow trout, the photosensitivity of the bleak extracts may be regarded as due to a red-sensitive and a red-insensitive component. By prolonged exposures to lights of long wavelength, the sensitive component could be almost entirely removed, leaving some insensitive component behind for investigation with short-wavelength bleaching lights. In this way DARTNALL (1952b) found that the red-insensitive component was a single pigment having λ_{max} at 510 $\pm$ 3 mμ. This pigment is probably identical with that, having λ_{max} at 507 $\pm$ 3 mμ, present in the rainbow trout.

The interpretation of the difference spectra obtained by partially bleaching the bleak extracts with long wavelength light was decidedly more difficult, however. The curves obtained had λ_{max} ranging from 545 mμ to 522 mμ, the majority lying between 539 mμ and 536 mμ. After analysing these results, DARTNALL (1955) concluded that the red-sensitive component consisted of two pigments; one with λ_{max} at 533 mμ and the other with λ_{max} at about 550 mμ.

In Fig. 6.8 the density spectra of pigments 510, 533 and 550 are scaled to the proportions in which they were present in the extract of Fig. 6.6. If the three density spectra are added together, the resulting curve is quite smooth and has a maximum at about 530 mμ; in fact (see dotted curve, Fig. 6.8) it closely resembles the density spectrum of pure pigment 533. This accounts for the close resemblance between the 'total' difference spectrum of this extract and that of a pike extract (Fig. 6.6) and emphasizes the need for testing the homogeneity of all retinal extracts, even in unpromising cases.

Over a period of twenty months five extracts were prepared from bleak. These had λ_{max} (after allowing for the $D_{min/max}$ ratios—see Fig. 2.6) ranging from 533 to 521 mμ. This variation was found to arise from differences in the relative proportions of the pigments 510, 533 and 550, and was largely caused by wide fluctuations in the amount of pigment 550. This was the least 'robust' pigment as judged by thermal stability. Thus the close resemblance between the

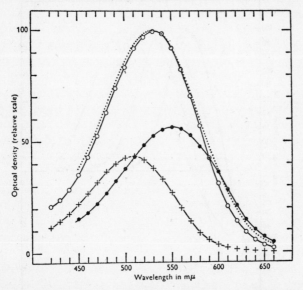

FIG. 6.8. Density spectra of the three photosensitive pigments in the bleak retina, scaled to the proportions in which they occurred in the extract of Fig. 6.6. +, pigment 510; O, pigment 533; ●, pigment 550. The dotted curve is the sum of these three curves brought, for comparison, to the same maximum (100) as that for pigment 533.

(*Dartnall*, 1955)

pike and bleak data (Fig. 6.6) was a coincidence: if the data for the extract with λ_{max} = 521 mμ had been chosen, a similarly close comparison could have been made with carp extracts (visual pigment 523).

COMPARISON BETWEEN DIFFERENCE SPECTRA OF THE VISUAL PIGMENTS

In Fig. 6.9, the difference spectra of pigments 467, 502 (visual purple), 533 and 562 (iodopsin) are shown on a uniform scale of wavelengths. The main feature brought out by this comparison is the broadening of the spectra as their location advances to longer wavelengths.

If, instead of a wavelength scale, a frequency scale is used, the difference spectra become very nearly of the same shape. This is shown in Fig. 6.10 in which the difference spectra have been shifted along the frequency axis so that their maxima correspond. Above

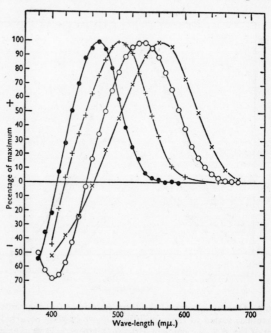

FIG. 6.9. Comparison of the difference spectra (wavelength abscissae) of four visual pigments. ●, pigment 467; +, pigment 502 (frog visual purple); ○, pigment 533; ×, pigment 562 or iodopsin (Bliss, 1946). (*Dartnall*, 1952a)

the 'base-line,' the curves are almost superimposable. Since the upper portion of a density spectrum approximates (particularly in alkaline solution) to the density spectrum of the pure visual pigment, this similarity suggests a corresponding agreement in shape between the density spectra of the visual pigments. DARTNALL (1953) therefore devised a nomogram by means of which the approximate density spectra of visual pigments of known λ_{max} could be constructed. The nomogram was based on the well-known density spectrum of visual pigment 502 (frog visual purple).

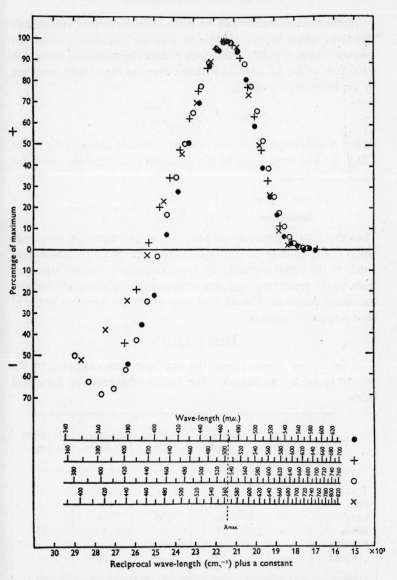

FIG. 6.10. Comparison of the difference spectra (frequency abscissae) of the same four visual pigments as in Fig. 6.9. The spectra have been shifted along the axis of abscissae so that their maxima coincide with that of pigment 467.

(*Dartnall*, 1952a)

Another generalization can be made with the help of Houstoun's equations which WEALE (1949a, b) used for calculating molecular weights (Chap. 3, p. 92). Houstoun related the molecular extinction coefficient at the λ_{max} (ε_{max}) with the shape of the density spectrum by the following equation,

$$\varepsilon_{max} = A \cdot \frac{p}{r} \frac{\lambda^2_{max}}{\lambda_{\frac{1}{2}max} - \lambda_{max}}$$

Where A is a constant and the other symbols are defined on p. 92 of Chap. 3. The term λ^2_{max} in this equation is an approximation for $\lambda_{max}\lambda_{\frac{1}{2}max}$. Now,

$$\frac{\lambda_{\frac{1}{2}max} - \lambda_{max}}{\lambda_{\frac{1}{2}max}\lambda_{max}} = \frac{1}{\lambda_{max}} - \frac{1}{\lambda_{\frac{1}{2}max}} = \nu_{max} - \nu_{\frac{1}{2}max}$$

Thus the ε_{max} is inversely proportional to the width (in frequency units) of the band at its semi-maximal height. Since the absorption bands of the visual pigments are approximately the same shape, this leads to the result that ε_{max}, the molecular extinction coefficients of the visual pigments, should have approximately the same value at their respective maxima.

DISCUSSION

So far, retinal extracts from five fish have been examined by the partial bleaching technique. The results obtained are tabulated below.

Fish	Pigment 467	Pigment 508*	Pigment 523	Pigment 533	Pigment 550
Tench	25	—	—	75	—
Pike	—	—	—	100	—
Carp	—	—	100	—	—
Bleak	—	25	—	50	25
Rainbow Trout	—	50	—	50	—

* Pigments 510 (bleak) and 507 (rainbow trout) have been assumed to be the same.

In the table, the figures represent the average proportions of the pigments present. Thus '100' indicates that only one pigment was found. The other figures compare the densities of the pigments at their respective λ_{max}, the sums being scaled to 100. The data are only approximate; considerable fluctuations were observed in different extracts made from the same species.

The photoproducts of these pigments had λ_{max} (estimated from the lower portions of the difference spectra) as listed below.

Pigment	λ_{max} of photoproduct
467	below 380 mμ
508	about 380 mμ
523	405–410 mμ
533	405–410 mμ
550	405–410 mμ

Now retinene$_1$ absorbs maximally at 380 mμ and retinene$_2$ in the 405–410 mμ region. This suggests that all the pigments found by the partial bleaching technique are based either on retinene$_1$ or on retinene$_2$. To this extent, the results are consistent with WALD'S findings (Chap. 2). Moreover, since the tench is often found in salt water, the presence of a retinene$_1$ pigment (467) in this fish is, perhaps, not surprising. Likewise, the euryhaline rainbow trout possesses both a retinene$_1$ (508) and a retinene$_2$ (533) pigment. The only unexpected result, therefore, is that for the bleak which has a retinene$_1$ pigment (508) in addition to two retinene$_2$ pigments (533 and 550), even though it is a fresh-water fish. This exception recalls the converse case of the marine tautog (Chap. 2, p. 36) which has a predominantly vitamin A$_2$ retina (WALD, 1939a).

Although the number of species so far examined by the partial bleaching method is too small to justify any generalizations, it is noteworthy that four out of five of the fish possess a pigment with λ_{max} at 533 mμ, and only one (the carp) a pigment with λ_{max} close to that assigned by WALD to 'porphyropsin' (522 mμ).

It is also evident that the visual pigment situation is more complex than envisaged by WALD (Chap. 5). If, for example, we regard the five pigments 467, 508, 523, 533 and 550 as rod pigments then, according to the classification on page 151, the protein moiety is, in each case, 'scotopsin.' Now the photoproducts obtained on bleaching the pigments suggest that 467 and 508 are retinene$_1$ pigments and hence should involve the specific isomer *neo*-retinene$_1$ *b*. Similarly, pigments 523, 533 and 550 are based on retinene$_2$, specifically *cis$_1$*-retinene$_2$. Thus pigments 467 and 508 would both be classified as '*neo*-retinene$_1$ *b*—scotopsin,' the identical composition accorded (p. 154) to 'rhodopsin' with λ_{max} at 500 mμ. The pigments 523, 533

179

and 550 would, similarly, all be classified as 'cis_1-retinene$_2$—scotopsin,' the same as 'porphyropsin' with λ_{max} at 522 mμ. If, on the other hand, we suppose that the five pigments are all cone pigments, then 467 and 508 should have the composition 'neo-retinene$_1$ b—photopsin' (i.e. the same as 'iodopsin' with $\lambda_{max} = 562$ mμ), and 523, 533 and 550, the composition 'cis_1-retinene$_2$—photopsin' (i.e. the same as 'cyanopsin' with $\lambda_{max} = 620$ mμ).

The present results suggest, therefore, that there may be active retinene$_1$ and retinene$_2$ isomers additional to those at present known, or that there are more 'opsins' than two.

REFERENCES

BAYLISS, L. E., LYTHGOE, R. J. and TANSLEY, K. (1936). Some new forms of visual purple found in sea fishes, with a note on the visual cells of origin. *Proc. roy. Soc. B*, **816**, 95–113.

BLISS, A. F. (1946). The chemistry of daylight vision. *J. gen. Physiol.*, **29**, 277–297.

BRIDGES, C. D. B. (1955). *The physical chemistry of visual pigments.* Ph.D. Thesis, London.

CRESCITELLI, F. and DARTNALL, H. J. A. (1954). A photosensitive pigment of the carp retina. *J. Physiol.*, **125**, 607–627.

DARTNALL, H. J. A. (1950). New photosensitive pigments from the tench retina. *Nature, Lond.*, **166**, 207–209.

DARTNALL, H. J. A. (1952a). Visual pigment 467, a photosensitive pigment present in tench retinae. *J. Physiol.*, **116**, 257–289.

DARTNALL, H. J. A. (1952b). A new visual pigment absorbing maximally at 510 mμ. *J. Physiol.*, **117**, 57P.

DARTNALL, H. J. A. (1953). The interpretation of spectral sensitivity curves. *Brit. med. Bull.*, **9**, 24–30.

DARTNALL, H. J. A. (1955). Visual pigments of the bleak (*alburnus lucidus*). *J. Physiol.*, **128**, 131–156.

GRANIT, R. (1941). A relation between rod and cone substances, based on scotopic and photopic spectra of *cyprinus, tinca, anguilla* and *testudo*. *Acta. Physiol. scand.*, **2**, 334–346.

KÖTTGEN, E. and ABELSDORFF, G. (1896). Absorption und Zersetzung des Sehpurpurs bei den Wirbeltieren. *Z. Psychol. Physiol. Sinnesorg.*, **12**, 161–184.

WALD, G. (1939a). On the distribution of vitamins A$_1$ and A$_2$. *J. gen. Physiol.*, **22**, 391–415.

WALD, G. (1939b). The porphyropsin visual system. *J. gen. Physiol.*, **22**, 775–794.

WEALE, R. A. (1949a). Absorption spectra, molecular weights and visual purple. *Nature, Lond.*, **163**, 916–917.

WEALE, R. A. (1949b). Absorption spectra, molecular weights and visual purple. *Nature, Lond.*, **164**, 959–960.

CHAPTER SEVEN

Other Methods of Studying Visual Pigments

The visual pigment investigations described in previous chapters have varied greatly in character, but they all have had one feature in common. In every case the starting material was obtained by treating retinae with an aqueous solution of a suitable 'solubilizer,' usually digitonin. By this means, the visual pigment or pigments were obtained in solution.

At present, the only way in which visual pigments can be characterized is by measuring their density spectra. When the pigments are in solution this can be done with a very high precision. Moreover, by bleaching the solutions in instalments and measuring the spectra at every stage, we obtain data which provide a powerful means of analysis.

Nevertheless the study of visual pigments in solution has some drawbacks. Thus, in order to take advantage of the precision of measurement possible, it is necessary for the solutions to be thermally stable. This means that unstable impurities, which would otherwise accompany the visual pigments, must first be removed by washing the retinae. It is possible that some visual pigments could be destroyed in this, and also in the subsequent extraction processes.

In the retina the visual pigments are presumably segregated in different structures (rods and cones) and are consequently insulated from each other. In solution the pigments can come into contact and perhaps interact. It is conceivable, for example, that, through an interchange of 'retinenes' and 'opsins,' new pigments, not present in the living retina, could be produced in solution.

Throughout this book the term 'visual pigment' has been applied to those light-sensitive substances (having a number of properties in common with known visual pigments) which are present in extracts. But in the light of these remarks we see that this is a chemical, rather than a physiological definition. Strictly speaking the visual significance of a pigment cannot be assumed until corresponding retinal or behavioural activity has been demonstrated.

Recently, new methods of investigation have been developed. These, whilst having difficulties of their own, are free from some of the above-mentioned disadvantages.

SUSPENSIONS OF VISUAL CELLS

As described in Chapter 1, the outer-segments of the retinal rods (and, presumably, of cones also) can be suspended in a 35–40 per cent sucrose solution. ARDEN (1954a) had the idea of using such suspensions as working material. If practicable, this offered a means of studying the visual pigments under conditions which more nearly approached their natural environment. Since most of our knowledge relates to the visual purple of frogs, ARDEN decided to work with these animals. This was a fortunate choice for suspensions of frog retinal outer-segments are stable, and retain their visual pigment for at least a week. This behaviour may be contrasted with that of some fish outer-segment suspensions which last only a few hours (DART-NALL, quoted by ARDEN, 1954a).

PHOTOMETRIC INVESTIGATION OF SUSPENSIONS

At first sight these suspensions would not seem to be very suitable material for exact spectrophotometric work. They scatter light very strongly and, in consequence, have a milky appearance, in which, however, can be detected a pinkish colour (changing to yellow after exposure to light) due to the visual pigment. Largely because of this scattering, such preparations transmit only a small proportion of the incident light (e.g. when of 0·5 cm thickness they transmit 1 in 250 of violet light and 1 in 25 of red light).

Optical density is defined as,

$$\log_{10} \frac{\text{intensity of incident light}}{\text{intensity of transmitted light}}$$

and consequently light which is scattered has the same effect, so far as the measurements are concerned, as that which is truly absorbed. The measured density is thus due in part to absorption but mainly to scattering. A typical suspension would have a density at 500 mμ of 2·0 before exposure to light and 1·8 after. The transmissions corresponding to these figures are 1 per cent before bleaching and 1·7 per cent after. Percentage transmissions of this magnitude cannot be measured with the desired accuracy. At longer wavelengths the situation improves a little, but at shorter wavelengths it rapidly worsens. Fortunately, this practical difficulty can be easily overcome by measuring the density of a suspension with reference to another sample of the same suspension. If the two optical cells are exactly the same and the samples are truly identical, zero density will be obtained at all wavelengths. If, now, one of the samples is exposed

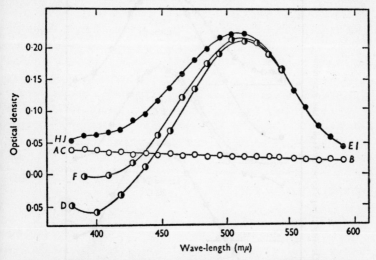

Fig. 7.1. The density-changes on bleaching a fresh suspension of frog visual cells. (Measurements made with respect to another portion of the same suspension.) *A–B* and *B–C*, two sets of interlaced measurements giving the 'base-line,' i.e. the initial difference between the two suspension samples. *D–E* and *E–F*, immediately after one sample had been bleached by white light. *H–I* and *I–J*, 3 hr later.

(*Arden*, 1954a)

to light and the measurements repeated, only the changes due to the bleaching of the visual pigment will be obtained. This supposes, of course, that the scattering properties of the suspensions are not affected by the bleaching. Direct measurement of the difference spectra in this way has the additional advantage that any small instability of the suspension is compensated by similar changes in the reference sample.

An example of these measurements is given in Fig. 7.1. Initially the difference between two suspension samples was small and neutral (*A–B*, *B–C*, Fig. 7.1). After exposing one of them to white light for

10 min, the measurements (*D–E, E–F*, Fig. 7.1) showed that bleaching of the photosensitive pigment and formation of a photoproduct had occurred. This photoproduct was thermally unstable, as is shown by the fact that the return measurements *E–F* did not retrace the path of

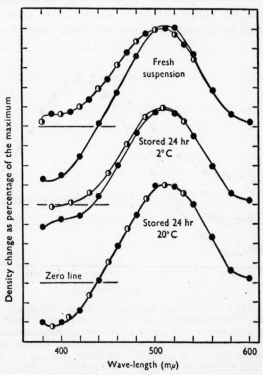

FIG. 7.2. Effect of storage on the difference spectra of frog visual cell suspensions. ●, measurements made from short to long wavelengths; ◑, 'return' measurements.

(*Arden*, 1954b)

the outward ones, *D–E*. Three hours later the measurements *H–I* and *I–J* were obtained. These showed that thermal decomposition of the initial photoproduct had been completed by that time.

EFFECT OF AGEING THE SUSPENSIONS

In Fig. 7.2 the difference spectra for a fresh suspension are compared with those obtained with suspensions stored for 24 hr at 2°C and 20°C respectively. After 24 hr at the higher temperature the thermal breakdown of the initial photoproduct (very noticeable in fresh suspensions) was no longer apparent. In suspensions stored for 3 days at 20°C the initial photoproduct was quite stable and the negative and positive limbs of the difference spectrum were then of nearly equal heights.

To investigate the carotenoids present in the suspensions, ARDEN (1954b) exposed a suspension to light, diluted it with Ringer-Locke and centrifuged it. After removing the supernatant, the precipitated outer segments were freeze-dried and then extracted with chloroform. The extract had an absorption band λ_{max} at 390 mμ (retinene$_1$). The same experiment was then carried out on another suspension except that the procedures subsequent to the bleaching were delayed for an hour. The chloroform extract in this case had an absorption band at 330 mμ which is characteristic of vitamin A$_1$.

These results strongly suggest that the initial photoproduct formed when suspensions are exposed to light is retinene$_1$ (or indicator yellow). In fresh suspensions this is then reduced to vitamin A$_1$, but during storage of suspensions the mechanism responsible for the reduction becomes inactive.

IS THERE AN EXTRA PIGMENT IN THE SUSPENSIONS?

The density maximum of pure (frog) visual purple is at 502 mμ. Difference spectra have λ_{max} displaced to slightly longer wavelengths. This arises from the 'overlap' between the absorption bands of pigment and photoproduct. In solution, the amount of displacement depends on the pH, for this determines the spectral location of the photoproduct absorption band. In acid solution the displacement is maximal and the λ_{max} is then at $c.$ 510 mμ.

Now the λ_{max} of the difference spectra of *suspensions* was also at $c.$ 510 mμ. ARDEN found that the pH of the suspending medium had no effect on the difference spectrum. This, no doubt, was due to the fact that the external pH did not alter conditions inside the suspended visual cells. Thus no direct evidence of the effect of pH could be obtained.

ARDEN considered that the high λ_{max} of suspension difference spectra could not be attributed entirely to a photoproduct artifact. Even in those cases where the initial photoproduct had been reduced to the colourless vitamin A (see Fig. 7.1, curve *HIJ*) the λ_{max} (505–510 mμ) was still higher than that for visual purple.

Could the high λ_{max} arise from physical causes? ARDEN (1954c) found that addition of sucrose to visual purple solutions was without effect on the λ_{max}. Again when suspensions were prepared using dextran—a high molecular weight polysaccharide, which is chemically inert, and which has a very low osmotic pressure—the same results as with sucrose were obtained. These experiments suggested that the nature of the suspending medium was not important. ARDEN concluded that the cause of the high λ_{max} lay either in the more intimate cell environment of the visual purple or in the presence of an additional photopigment in the suspensions.

To investigate the latter possibility, the homogeneity of the suspensions was tested by the method of partial bleaching. Partial bleachings were carried out with lights of dominant wavelengths 480, 530, 580 and 620 mμ. Bleaching was, in each case, then completed by exposing the suspension to white light. These experiments yielded difference spectra which, though substantially alike, nevertheless showed minor differences. ARDEN interpreted them as due to the presence of a second photosensitive pigment having λ_{max} in the green (at $c.$ 535 mμ) and a much sharper absorption band than visual purple. He supported this interpretation by the following experiment. When 2 per cent digitonin solution was added to a suspension, the outer limbs were lysed, releasing visual pigment into solution. Soon after the addition of digitonin (within 30 min) the difference spectrum obtained on bleaching was the same as for the original suspension (i.e. λ_{max} at 510 mμ). Two hours after the addition, however, the difference spectrum resembled that for visual purple in solution (λ_{max} near to 500 mμ). The value of this experiment as supporting evidence for the extra pigment is weakened, however, by our ignorance of the rates of lysis of the visual cells.

PHOTOMICROGRAPHIC DENSITOMETRY OF VISUAL PIGMENTS IN AN EXCISED RETINA

DENTON and WYLLIE (1955) devised a method for measuring the optical densities of pigments present in excised retinae. They used freshly dissected retinae of dark adapted frogs (*Rana temporia*). The dissections were carried out under Ringer's solution in very dim light (usually red) and each retina was floated, rod side upwards, into a well on a microscope slide.

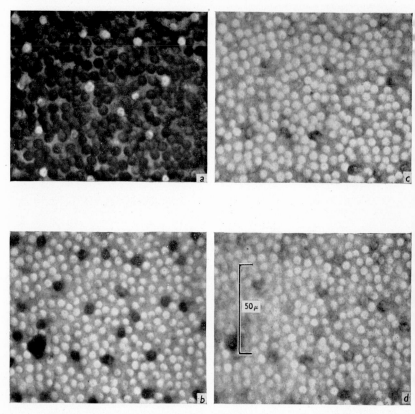

PLATE 7.1. Photomicrographs, all of the same part of one frog's retina taken (a) in green and (b) in blue light before bleaching; (c) in green and (d) in blue light, after bleaching.

(*Denton and Wyllie*, 1955)

When such preparations were examined microscopically in the usual way, two kinds of rods could be seen. The great majority were pink and owed their colour to visual purple. A small proportion, however, were grass green in colour, an observation first made by BOLL (1876) and confirmed by KÜHNE (1878).

The two kinds of rods are well shown in the photomicrographs (Plate 7.1 (a), (b), (c), (d)) of the same part of one frog's retina. Plate 7.1 (a) was taken in green light (520 mμ) before the preparation was bleached. The dark circles are an end-on view of the numerous 'visual purple' rods, which absorb green light very strongly. The light circles are the green rods which do not absorb this light. In blue light (420 mμ) this picture is reversed: the visual purple rods are almost transparent while the green rods absorb strongly and appear as dark circles. Plates 7.1 (c) and 7.1 (d) were taken in the green and blue light, respectively, after the preparation had been bleached by exposing it to intense white light.

METHODS

By careful standardization of their techniques, DENTON and WYLLIE were able to make a number of important quantitative observations. In all their experiments a $\frac{2}{3}$ in. microscope objective of N.A. 0·28 was used and the photographs were taken on Ilford HP3 35 mm roll film with a constant exposure of 10 sec. The magnification from retina to film was 36 diameters. The film was developed in I.D. 11. The source of light was a 48 W, 8 V tungsten lamp, underrun at 7·5 V.

The principle of their quantitative methods was as follows. A suitable colour filter, to isolate the required spectral band, was inserted in front of the light source. This was then switched on and three photographs of the unbleached preparation were taken. These differed only in that neutral filters of densities $D + 0·3$, $D + 0·2$ and $D + 0·1$ had been placed in turn beneath the substage condenser. The neutral and colour filters were then both removed thus exposing the preparation to intense white light. Bleaching was completed in a few seconds but the exposure was continued for 2 min. Ten minutes later the bleached preparation was again photographed a number of times with the colour filter and various neutral filters in position. It was then possible to ascertain what change in neutral filter exactly matched the density change caused by bleaching. For example, if a photograph of the unbleached retina through neutral filter $D + 0·1$

exactly matched one made after bleaching through neutral filter $D + 0.6$, this would show that the density change due to bleaching had been 0·5. In this case the photographs taken through $D + 0.2$ before bleaching and through $D + 0.7$ after would also match, and so on.

When it was desired to measure the average retinal density changes on bleaching, the matching was done by means of a photoelectric densitomer. Small portions of the films were interposed between a constant source and a photoelectric cell. In these measurements it was immaterial whether the image of the photoreceptors was sharply in focus (as in Plate 7.1) or so far out of focus as to result in a uniform density over the whole film.

When the changes in individual photoreceptors were required, the image had to be in accurate focus. Print enlargements of the films were made and the comparisons were done visually with the aid of a low-power binocular microscope.

MEASUREMENTS ON INDIVIDUAL PHOTORECEPTORS

The results of measurements made on individual rods in six different frogs' retinae are given in the following table.

The density changes on bleaching given in the table refer to

No. of Expt.	Pink rods			% of green rods
	Individual rod density change (520 mμ)	Average density change (520 mμ)	% retinal area covered by pink rods	
1	0·65	0·42	55	5·9
2	0·67	0·48	64	7·5
3	0·57	0·44	59	7·1
4	0·71	0·46	50	14·1
5	0·83	0·49	67	6·5
6	0·50	0·38	58	7·5
Av. for retinae 1–6	0·66	0·45	59	8·2

measurements made with light transmitted by an Ilford 604 filter (maximum transmission at 520 mμ).

From the known absorption spectrum of frogs' visual purple and the spectral transmission of the filter, DENTON and WYLLIE calculated that to obtain the corresponding density at the maximum (500 mμ) these values should be increased by 15·7 per cent, i.e. to 0·76 for the individual rods and to 0·52 for the retinal average. This calculation assumes that the photoproduct in DENTON and WYLLIE'S experiments does not appreciably absorb light of wavelength 520 mμ. If, however, the product is the same as that in neutral *solution* a further increase of 9 per cent in these figures would be required.

These values are a good deal higher than have been previously quoted for frogs. Thus WALD (1938), after extracting the visual purple from bull-frog retinae (*Rana catesbiana*) and measuring its absorption in solution, calculated that it would have a density at 500 mμ of 0·21 *in situ*, if spread uniformly over the retina. DARTNALL (1953) arrived at a similar figure (0·25) for the visual purple of *R. temporaria*. HUBBARD (1954), calculated from BRODA, GOODEVE and LYTHGOE'S (1938) data that, in *R. esculenta*, the density at 500 mμ along the axis of the outer limb of a rod was 0·50.

The difference between WALD and DARTNALL'S values on the one hand and HUBBARD'S on the other is due to the fact that the rods do not cover the whole area of the retina. DENTON and WYLLIE were able to make a quantitative allowance for this. Thus the rods cover only 59 per cent of the retinal surface, and consequently WALD'S and DARTNALL'S values of 0·21 and 0·25 should be multiplied by 1/0·59 giving 0·36 and 0·42 respectively, in comparison with HUBBARD'S value of 0·50.

Yet a further factor needs to be considered before these results can be compared with DENTON and WYLLIE'S. The molecules of visual purple are regularly oriented in the rods. DENTON and WYLLIE estimated that the oriented visual purple molecules would absorb 50 per cent more light than they would in a random state (e.g. in solution). This factor, applied to the results of WALD, DARTNALL and HUBBARD give the values 0·53, 0·63 and 0·75, respectively, in comparison with DENTON and WYLLIE'S value, 0·76.

THE GREEN RODS

In the photographs of unbleached and bleached retinae (see, for example, Plate 7.1) the spaces between rods and the visual purple rods both provided standards of reference. From them, DENTON and WYLLIE (1955) were able to estimate roughly the absorption characteristics of the green rods.

In the unbleached state, the green rods absorbed strongly in the blue (400–440 mμ), moderately in the yellow and red (560–680 mμ) but hardly at all in the green (490–520 mμ). These characteristics thus account for their green colour. After being bleached by white light, the green rods became much paler in the blue but darker in the green (see Plate 7.1) while in the yellow and red they hardly changed. This accounts for their grey colour when bleached.

Using the loss in density in the blue (max. at 430 mμ) as a criterion of bleaching, DENTON and WYLLIE found that the green rods were readily bleached by blue light but were hardly affected by green light. They were also insensitive to deep red light (wavelengths longer than 650 mμ). From this DENTON and WYLLIE concluded that the green rods would act as blue-sensitive receptors, and that the absorption band in the range 560–680 mμ was due to the presence of a light-stable pigment in these rods.

KÜHNE (1878), however, had stated that the green rods were especially sensitive to red light. Possibly KÜHNE's red light contained shorter wavelengths than DENTON and WYLLIE's ($>$ 650 mμ). Unfortunately the latter authors did not report the effect of light within the range 560–650 mμ. If such light should be effective in bleaching, i.e. in causing loss of density at 430 mμ, this would indicate that the light-stable pigment responsible for absorption at the long wavelengths acts as a photosensitizer for the bleaching of pigment 430. In this event the green rods would be sensitive to light within the range 560–650 mμ as well as to blue light.

PRESENCE OF GREEN-ROD PIGMENT IN EXTRACTS

Partial bleaching experiments carried out on a digitonin extract of frogs' retinae have suggested the presence of a small amount of photosensitive pigment with λ_{max} 430–440 mμ (DARTNALL, unpublished). The frogs were *Rana esculenta*, a species closely related to *R. temporaria* used in DENTON and WYLLIE's work. The results are shown in Fig. 7.3. In Fig. 7.3 (A), curve 1 is the density spectrum of the unbleached extract; curve 2 same after 2 hr exposure to yellow light (570 mμ); curves 3 and 4 after further exposures of 2 and 1 hr, respectively, to the same yellow light, and finally, curve 5 after exposure to white light. The difference spectra between each curve

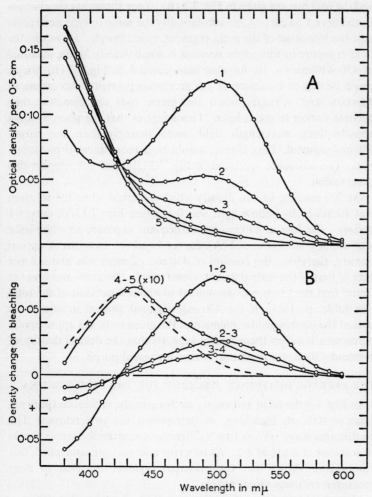

Fig. 7.3. Evidence for a blue-sensitive pigment in the retinal extract of *Rana esculenta*. (A) Curve 1, density spectrum of unexposed extract; curves 2, 3 and 4, density spectra of the extract after 2, 4 and 5 hr exposure, respectively, to yellow light (570 mμ) which removes most of the visual purple; curve 5, after exposure to white light. (B) Difference spectra constructed from the (A) curves. The dashed curve (obtained by correcting 4–5 for the contribution of residual visual purple) is the density spectrum of the blue-sensitive pigment.

(*Dartnall, unpublished*)

and the next one are given in Fig. 7.3 (B). They show that the changes from curve 1 to curve 4 are substantially the same in type and represent the bleaching of the main pigment, visual purple. However, the final exposure to white light resulted in small density losses, maximal at 430–440 mμ ($\times$ 10, for clearness, curve 4–5, Fig. 7.3 (B)) which could be due to bleaching of the green-rod pigment. According to DENTON and WYLLIE, when the green rods are bleached they become darker in green light. This suggests that the photoproduct absorbs long wavelength light more strongly than the parent 430 mμ pigment. This, if true, would be a most unusual phenomenon. The difference spectrum in Fig. 7.3 (B) does not support this observation.

At 500 mμ, the loss in density which occurred when the solution was bleached by yellow light was 0·115 (see Fig. 7.3 (A), curves 1 and 4). The loss at 430 mμ on subsequent exposure to white light was about 0·0064 (Fig. 7.3 (A), curves 4 and 5). In terms of optical density, therefore, the amount of 430 mμ pigment was about 6 per cent of that of the main pigment, visual purple. DENTON and WYLLIE found that the green rods amounted to about 8 per cent of the total (see table, p. 188). If the 430 mμ pigment present in solution is indeed the photosensitive pigment of the green rods, the approximate agreement between these figures suggests that the optical density of pigment 430 *in situ* is similar to that for visual purple.

THE AVERAGE DIFFERENCE SPECTRUM FOR THE FROG'S RETINA

In Fig. 7.4 the filled and empty circles give the difference spectrum (max = 100) on bleaching, as determined for two retinae. The continuous curve is LYTHGOE's difference spectrum for visual purple in solution at a pH of 8·5. As DENTON and WYLLIE concluded, this comparison shows that the principal pigment involved in their measurements was visual purple.

Now the λ_{max} of the retinal data is at 510 mμ rather than 500 mμ. This cannot be due to the green rods for the λ_{max} of the photosensitive pigment, which they contain, is at 430 mμ.

The retinal difference spectrum closely agrees with that, found by ARDEN, for suspensions of the frog's photoreceptors (Fig. 7.2). This suggests that the 'extra' pigment (p. 185) which ARDEN considered was present in his suspensions could likewise be responsible for the displacement to λ_{max} 510 mμ of the retinal data. Now DENTON and WYLLIE did not mention any rods other than the 'pink' (visual purple) or 'green' ones, and the latter were almost transparent to green light. We must therefore suppose that ARDEN'S 'extra' pigment either coexists with visual purple in the pink rods, or, that it is a cone pigment. The frog's retina is known to contain cones. These, although they were out of focus in DENTON and WYLLIE'S photographs, would contribute to the changes occurring on bleaching.

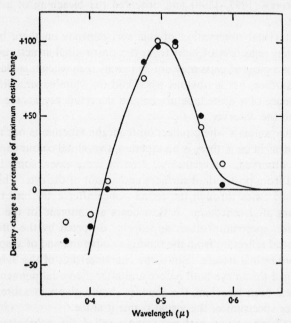

FIG. 7.4. Comparison between the difference spectrum of frog visual purple in solution at pH 8·5 (continuous line) with that in intact retinae (○ and ● give the spectral density changes of two retinae on bleaching with white light).

(*Denton and Wyllie*, 1955)

DENTON and WYLLIE used the spaces between rods in their photographs (Plate 7.1) as a standard for assessing the absorption characteristics of the green rods. If, however, the spaces were occupied by out-of-focus cones containing a photosensitive pigment of λ_{max} 535 mμ, or thereabouts, the bleaching of this pigment would result in the spaces becoming much more transparent to green light. By contrast, the green rods might then seem to have become darker in the green as the result of bleaching.

OBSERVATIONS OF VISUAL PIGMENTS IN LIVING RETINAE

In certain cases it is possible to see the visual pigment in a living animal's eye. Thus, simply by looking through an ophthalmoscope into the eyes of crocodiles and certain fish which have white tapeta, ABELSDORFF (1897, 1898) had observed the bleaching of a purple pigment.

Direct visual observation of this sort depends on there being a substantial reflection of light from the post-retinal structures. The colour of a piece of glass may not be readily seen when it is placed on a dark surface, but is obvious when laid on white paper. Similarly the presence of a white tapetum behind the retina reveals the retinal colour to the observer.

In other animals where reflection from the tapetum is not neutral or where, as in man, there is no tapetum, the retinal colour cannot be directly observed. Nevertheless, even in these cases, some light is reflected from post-retinal surfaces and so out of the eye. This light has passed twice through the retina—once after entry into the eye and again after reflection. It thus bears an 'imprint' of the retinal absorption spectrum; albeit an imprint distorted by the effects of non-neutral reflection from the fundus or tapetum, and of absorption in the pre-retinal tissues. But if the characteristics of the light were determined for an eye both before and after the visual pigment of its retina had been bleached, the changes should give a measure of the difference spectrum of the visual pigment alone.

In 1952, BRINDLEY and WILLMER applied the ophthalmoscope principle of ABELSDORFF in a quantitative sense to the human eye. The light from a monochromator was divided so that part entered the subject's eye and the rest traversed a comparison pathway which included a neutral wedge filter. By a suitable adjustment of the wedge, the intensity of the comparison beam was matched with that reflected from the fundus of the subject's eye. This was done for several wavelength settings of the monochromator. By comparing the reflection of light from the macular with that from a peripheral area of the retina, BRINDLEY and WILLMER estimated the density of macular pigmentation. They also attempted, with partial success, to detect the bleaching of visual purple in the dark-adapted periphery of the retina.

Another investigation which indirectly stimulated *in vivo* studies

194

of the visual pigments was that of GUNTER, HARDING and STILES (1951) on the spectral reflexion factors of the cat's tapetum. These measurements which had been carried out on excised tapeta prompted WEALE (1952, 1953a) to study intact tapeta of decerebrate cats.

The results obtained by BRINDLEY and WILLMER encouraged RUSHTON (1952) to devise more sensitive arrangements for the *in vivo* detection of visual pigments. Similarly, the success of the tapetal

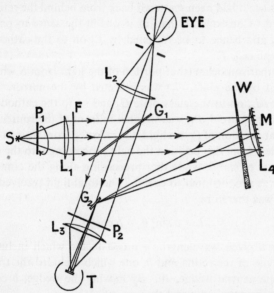

FIG. 7.5. Optical arrangement of apparatus for measuring density changes in the retinae of animals. *S*, light source; L_1, L_2, L_3 and L_4, lenses; G_1 and G_2, glass plates; *M*, mirror; *W*, neutral wedge; P_1, rotating polaroid; P_2, stationary polaroid; *F*, filter; *T*, photocell.
(*Rushton, Campell, Hagins and Brindley*, 1955)

investigations led WEALE (1953b) to the study of the whole eye and hence of the changes occurring in the visual pigment layer. In the last three years RUSHTON and his colleagues in Cambridge, and WEALE in London have laid the foundations of new techniques which have already yielded important results.

APPARATUS

A diagram of the apparatus used by RUSHTON and his colleagues for experiments with decerebrate rabbits or with excised eyes is shown in Fig. 7.5. The light from *S*, a car headlamp bulb passed through a collimating lens, L_1, and one of a set of interference filters, F. It then fell upon a glass plate, G_1, at the polarizing angle. The reflected (and hence completely plane polarized) portion of the beam was focussed by L_2 upon the cornea of the rabbit's eye and illumined a circular patch of retina. The unwanted light, specularly reflected from the corneal surface and from L_2, was plane polarized and was extinguished by a suitably orientated polaroid, P_2. The wanted light, however, since it had been scattered back from behind the retina, was depolarized. Consequently half of it was in the sense to pass both G_1 and P_2 and hence to be focussed by L_3 on to the cathode of a photoelectric cell, T.

The comparison beam (that portion of the light from S which was transmitted by the plate, G_1) was reflected by the mirror, M, and focussed by L_4 on to the glass plate G_2 and so to the cathode of T.

A rotating polaroid, P_1, was situated in front of the source, S. At one angular position of P_1, no light was reflected from G_1 into the eye. At an angle θ from this position the light proceeding into the eye was proportional to $\sin^2 \theta$, while that proceeding along the comparison pathway was proportional to $\cos^2 \theta$. The total light received by the photocell was therefore

$$I = a \sin^2 \theta + b \cos^2 \theta$$

where, for a given wavelength, a was a factor which included the transmissivity of the retina and b, one which included the transmissivity of the neutral wedge, W. By moving the wedge, b could be adjusted to be equal to a and then,

$$I = a(\sin^2 \theta + \cos^2 \theta) = a$$

The photocell output was condenser-coupled to an oscilloscope. The polaroid, P_1, rotated at about 40 rev/sec so that an 80 cycle A.C. wave was normally seen on the screen. By moving the wedge, W, the amplitude of this wave could be reduced to zero; at which point, b was equal to a. The wedge reading was then recorded. Any change in the optical density of the visual pigment in the retina caused a change in a with the consequent reappearance of a sine wave upon the screen. By making an equal change in b, however, the balance could be restored. Since the test beam passed twice through the retina, and the comparison beam twice through the wedge, any change in visual pigment density was measured directly by the change in wedge density required to eliminate the sine wave.

196

In WEALE'S apparatus (Fig. 7.6) the light emerging from the exit slit, S, of a monochromator was rendered parallel by the lens L_1, and then fell normally on to the face of a glass cube P composed of two

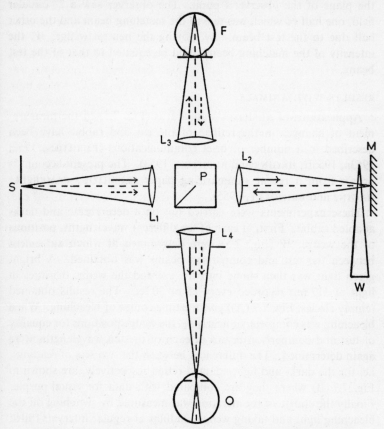

FIG. 7.6. Apparatus for the measurement of spectral reflectivity of the tapetum and hence of changes in the concentration of visual pigments in the retina. S, exit slit of monochromator; L_1, L_2, L_3 and L_4, lenses; P, glass cube with half diagonal plane silvered; W, neutral wedge; M, magnesium oxide surface; F, the animal's eye; O, observer's eye.

(*After Weale*, 1953a)

45° prisms cemented together. Half the surface of the diagonal plane of P had been silvered. Consequently the light from the monochromator was divided into two, a matching beam which was focussed on to the magnesium oxide surface, M, and a test beam which was focussed on to the animal's fundus, F. After their respective reflections from these surfaces, the two beams were brought alongside each other once more by the action of the cube P, and focussed by L_4 in the plane of the observer's pupil. The observer saw a 2° circular field, one half of which was due to the matching beam and the other half due to the test beam. By moving the neutral wedge, W, the intensity of the matching beam could be equated to that of the test beam.

RESULTS WITH ANIMALS

Applications of RUSHTON's apparatus (Fig. 7.5) to the measurement of changes in the retinae of the cat and rabbit have been described in a number of brief communications (RUSHTON, 1952, 1953a, 1953b; HAGINS and RUSHTON, 1953). The present account is drawn from a recent summarizing paper (RUSHTON, CAMPBELL, HAGINS and BRINDLEY, 1955).

These experiments were carried out on a decerebrate and dark-adapted rabbit. First, at each of ten different wavelengths, positions of the wedge, W (Fig. 7.5) were determined at which agreement between the test and comparison beams was obtained. A bright green light was then shone into the eye and the wedge densities in light of 517 mμ recorded every 15 or 30 sec. The results obtained (empty circles, Fig. 7.7 (A)) give the time course of bleaching. When bleaching was complete, or nearly so, the wedge positions for equality of test and comparison beams at each of the ten wavelengths were again determined. The differences between the two sets of readings, i.e. for the dark- and light-adapted retina respectively, are shown in Fig. 7.7 (B) where they are compared with data for visual purple. Finally the course of regeneration was measured by switching off the bleaching light and taking wedge readings at regular intervals (filled circles, Fig. 7.7 (A)). These measurements were made in light of 517 mμ applied for about 5 sec every 5 min. Tests showed that in 5 sec the measuring light caused less than 0·0002 density unit of bleaching.

Results of a similar nature were also obtained by WEALE. Thus WEALE (1953b) recorded the regeneration of visual pigment in the retinas of light-adapted, decerebrate cats. In most cases the rate of regeneration was slow, the half-return period being about 20 min (compare Fig. 7.7 (A)). The difference spectrum for the slow changes had a maximum at about 495 mμ (Fig. 7.8) and indicated that, in the

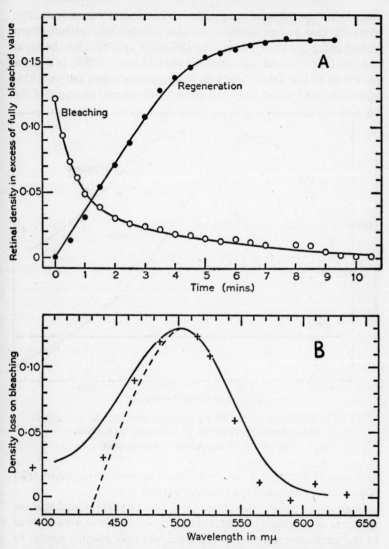

FIG. 7.7. (A) Time courses of bleaching and regeneration in the retina of the decerebrate rabbit. Measurements made with light of 517 mμ. (B) Difference spectrum (+) of the retinal bleaching compared with the density spectrum (full curve) and difference spectrum at pH 5·5 (dashed curve) of frog's visual purple.

(*Redrawn after Rushton, Campbell, Hagins and Brindley, 1955*) main, visual purple was being regenerated. In a few instances, however, the rate of regeneration was exceedingly fast, the half-return period being less than 1 min. The difference spectrum for the rapid changes (Fig. 7.8) had λ_{max} at $c.$ 550 mμ (WEALE, 1953c). In a paper published at the time of writing, WALD, BROWN and SMITH (1955) have reported that at 10°C and pH 6·5 the velocity constant of the

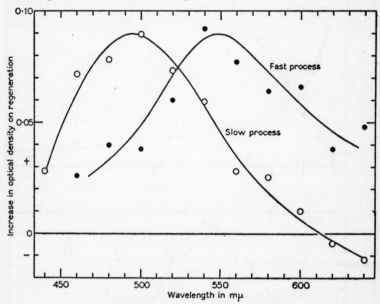

FIG. 7.8. Difference spectra for the (normal) slow and the (occasional) fast regenerative processes in the living cat's retina.
(*Weale*, 1953b *and private communication*)

synthesis of iodopsin ($\lambda_{max} = 562$ mμ) in solution is more than 500 times that for rhodopsin (visual purple).

In an investigation of the guinea-pig, WEALE (1955) found that the spectrum of the density changes occurring when retinae were exposed to the unselective action of white light was only roughly similar to that of visual purple. The 'irregularities' suggested that other pigments might be involved as well. WEALE therefore used the method of partial bleaching in order to test the homogeneity of the retinal pigment. The results of one experiment are shown in Fig. 7.9. The upper part of Fig. 7.9 gives the spectrum density changes when a dark-adapted retina was partially bleached with blue light. In the lower part of the figure are shown the additional changes when the bleaching was completed by white light. The total changes on bleaching were always the same (within experimental error) whether the retinae were bleached by a single exposure to white light or first partly bleached with coloured light and then with white light.

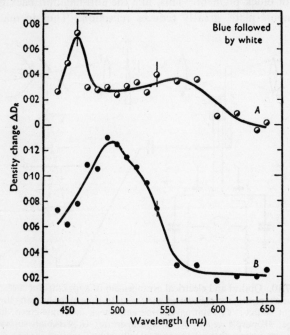

FIG. 7.9. Difference spectra of the density changes caused in albino guinea pigs' retinae by (A) partial bleaching by blue light, and (B) further bleaching to completion by white light.

(*Weale*, 1955)

These experiments suggest that the guinea-pig retina contains photosensitive pigments in addition to visual purple, but it is not possible, as yet, to unravel the absorption characteristics of the additional pigments.

RESULTS WITH MAN

Results which have been obtained with human subjects (CAMPBELL and RUSHTON, 1954; RUSHTON and CAMPBELL, 1954; RUSHTON, CAMPBELL, HAGINS and BRINDLEY, 1955) are separately

14   201

reviewed here, partly because of their greater intrinsic interest and partly because special apparatus had to be designed in order to obtain them.

In the case of the cat and rabbit (for example) there is a strong reflexion from post-retinal structures. In man, however, the retina is lined with black pigment. This, like the anti-halation backing of a photographic plate, greatly reduces reflection. Thus in man little

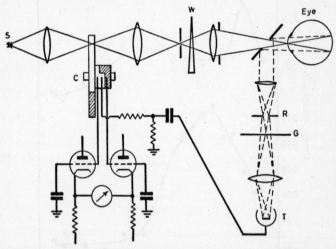

FIG. 7.10. Optical and electrical arrangement of apparatus for measuring the changes in the concentration of visual purple in the human retina. *S*, light source; *C*, rotating transparent wheel, half blue-green, half orange; *W*, purple wedge; *R*, variable aperture; *G*, glass plate supporting an opacity to extinguish the corneal reflexion; *T*, multiplier photocell.

(*Rushton, Campbell, Hagins and Brindley*, 1955)

light emerges from the post-retinal surface of the eye and reflections and scatter from other surfaces are, in comparison, much more serious. Further complications arise from the involuntary head and eye movements, which cannot be eliminated in a conscious subject.

To overcome these difficulties, RUSHTON and CAMPBELL (1954) designed special apparatus with which retinal densities could be compared in orange and blue-green light sent in succession along the same optical path. In this apparatus (Fig. 7.10) light from a source passed through a transparent wheel, one half of which was blue-green and the other half orange. On rotating the wheel (at 20 rev/sec) the light transmitted was thus alternately blue-green and orange.

It was focussed on to the subject's cornea through a hole in the silvering of a cover slip and illumined a circular patch of retina of 2° diameter. The light reflected from behind this illumined area passed out of the eye and (via the optical path shown by dashed lines in Fig. 7.10) on to the cathode of a multiplier photocell. The alternate signals from the photocell (corresponding to blue-green and to orange light, respectively) were kept separate by passing them through

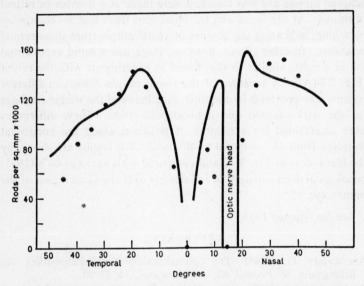

FIG. 7.11. Comparison between visual purple density in the human eye (filled circles) and the population distribution of the retinal rods. (*Rushton, Campbell, Hagins and Brindley*, 1955)

a commutator on the shaft of the colour wheel and so, through the grids of two cathode followers, to condensers acting as reservoirs. A galvanometer was connected across the cathodes to give a null indication when the signal levels were equal.

Initially the photocell outputs for the orange and blue-green lights were adjusted to equality by a suitable movement of a blue setting-wedge, not shown in Fig. 7.10. Now nearly all the light falling on the photocell had passed twice through the retina. A change in the density of retinal visual purple would not greatly change the strength of the orange signal for visual purple is nearly transparent to orange light. But the strength of the blue-green signal would be greatly affected. Thus any change in visual purple density would upset the null balance of the galvanometer. This could then be restored by a suitable movement of a purple wedge, W, in Fig. 7.10, placed in the path of the incident light. In this way any decrease or increase in visual purple could be followed by noting the purple-wedge positions required for balance.

Measurements of the changes which occurred when the dark-adapted human eye was bleached were made at a number of retinal positions. At the fovea and the blind spot there was no change on bleaching, indicating the absence of visual purple from these retinal positions. In other places, however, there was a rapid exponential fall in density, similar to that found in experiments with the rabbit (Fig. 7.7 (A)). A measure of the visual purple density in different regions was provided by the difference between the wedge readings for the dark-adapted and light-adapted retina. These differences were ascertained for a number of positions along the horizontal meridian from 45° temporal to 40° nasal. The results are shown by the black dots in Fig. 7.11 and compared with ØSTERBERG'S (1935) histological determination of rod density over the same region of the human eye.

London, August 1955.

REFERENCES

ABELSDORFF, G. (1896). Die ophthalmoskopische Erkennbarkeit des Sehpurpurs. *Z. Psychol. Physiol. Sinnesorg.*, **14**, 77–90.

ABELSDORFF, G. (1898). Physiologische Beobachtungen am Auge der Krokodile. *Arch. Anat. u. Physiol. (Physiol.)*, 155–167.

ARDEN, G. B. (1954a). Light-sensitive pigment in the visual cells of the frog. *J. Physiol.*, **123**, 377–385.

ARDEN, G. B. (1954b). The dark reactions in visual cell suspensions. *J. Physiol.*, **123**, 386–395.

ARDEN, G. B. (1954c). A narrow-band pigment present in visual cell suspensions. *J. Physiol.*, **123**, 396–408.

BOLL, F. (1876). Sull' anatomia e fisiologia della retina. *Mem. Acad. Lincei*, **1**, 371–393.

BRINDLEY, G. S. and WILLMER, E. N. (1952). The reflexion of light from the macular and peripheral fundus oculi in man. *J. Physiol.*, **116**, 350–356.

BRODA, E. E., GOODEVE, C. F. and LYTHGOE, R. J. (1938). The weight of the chromophore carrier in the visual purple molecule. *J. Physiol.*, **98**, 397–404.

CAMPBELL, F. W. and RUSHTON, W. A. H. (1954). The measurement of rhodopsin in the human eye. *J. Physiol.*, **126**, 36–37P.

DARTNALL, H. J. A. (1953). The interpretation of spectral sensitivity curves. *Brit. med. Bull.*, **9**, 24–30.

DENTON, E. J. and WYLLIE, J. H. (1955). Study of the photosensitive pigments in the pink and green rods of the frog. *J. Physiol.*, **127**, 81–89.

GUNTER, R., HARDING, H. G. W. and STILES, W. S. (1951). Spectral reflexion factor of the cat's tapetum. *Nature, Lond.*, **168**, 293–294.

HAGINS, W. A. and RUSHTON, W. A. H. (1953). The measurement of rhodopsin in the decerebrate albino rabbit. *J. Physiol.*, **120**, 61P.

HUBBARD, R. (1954). The molecular weight of rhodopsin and the nature of the rhodopsin-digitonin complex. *J. gen. Physiol.*, **37**, 381–399.

KÜHNE, W. (1878). *On the photochemistry of the retina and on visual purple.* Ed. with notes by M. Foster, London, Macmillan.

ØSTERBERG, G. (1935). Topography of the layer of rods and cones in the human retina. *Acta Ophthalm. Suppl.*, **6**, 1–103.

RUSHTON, W. A. H. (1952). Apparatus for analysing the light reflected from the eye of the cat. *J. Physiol.*, **117**, 47P.

RUSHTON, W. A. H. (1953a). *Aspects of retinal physiology.* Pub. Inst. Biofísica, Rio.

RUSHTON, W. A. H. (1953b). The measurement of rhodopsin in the living eye. *Acta. Physiol. scand.*, **29**, 16–18.

RUSHTON, W. A. H. and CAMPBELL, F. W. (1954). Measurement of rhodopsin in the living human eye. *Nature, Lond.*, **174**, 1096–1097.

RUSHTON, W. A. H., CAMPBELL, F. W., HAGINS, W. A. and BRINDLEY, G. S. (1955). The bleaching and regeneration of rhodopsin in the living eye of the albino rabbit and of man. *Optica Acta*, **1**, 183–190.

WALD, G. (1938). On rhodopsin in solution. *J. gen. Physiol.*, **21**, 795–832. (This reference, quoted by Denton and Wyllie, (1955), gives the mean *in situ* density of visual purple in the bull frog retina as 0·178.)

WALD, G., BROWN, P. K. and SMITH, P. H. (1955). Iodopsin. *J. gen. Physiol.*, **38**, 623–681.

WEALE, R. A. (1952). Tapetal reflexion and its influence on some visual functions of the cat. *J. Physiol.*, **118**, 43P. (Oral communication.)

WEALE, R. A. (1953a). The spectral reflectivity of the cat's tapetum measured *in situ*. *J. Physiol.*, **119**, 30–42.

WEALE, R. A. (1953b). Photochemical reactions in the living cat's retina. *J. Physiol.*, **122**, 322–331.

WEALE, R. A. (1953c). Slow and rapid regeneration in the living cat's retina. *J. Physiol.*, **122**, 11P.

WEALE, R. A. (1955). Bleaching experiments on eyes of living guinea-pigs. *J. Physiol.*, **127**, 572–586.

Author Index

Subject Index

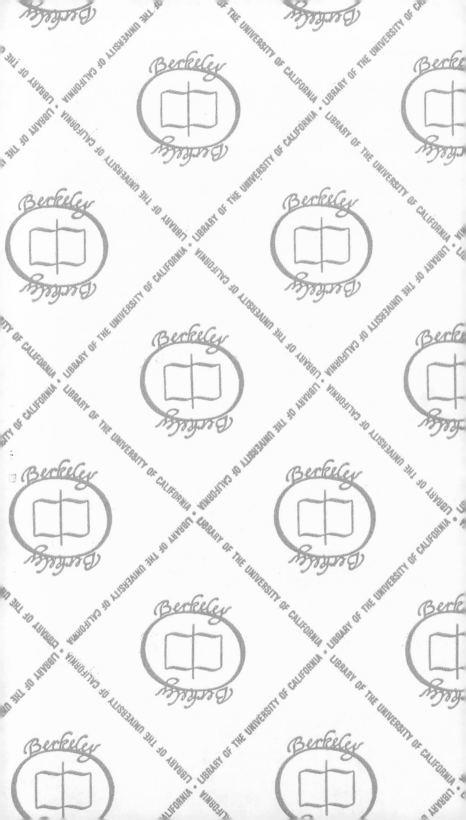